Macmillan
English
Practice Book

Mary Bowen
Louis Fidge
Liz Hocking
Wendy Wren

macmillan
education

Unit 1

Comprehension

1 **Read pages 8–9 again. Number each sentence in order.**

_____   Lek said there were more fish away from land.

__1__   Daeng was worried.

_____   Lek put the fishing net into the water.

_____   It was perfect weather for fishing.

_____   The fishing net was caught on something.

_____   Daeng said they would look for fish close to Si Racha.

_____   The boat stopped moving.

_____   Daeng stopped the boat where there were no rocks.

2 **Answer the questions.**

1 Write what you know about Daeng.

_____

_____

_____

_____

_____

2 Write what you know about Lek.

_____

_____

_____

_____

_____

Vocabulary

Remember. **Adjectives** are describing words.

1 **Find these *adjectives* in the wordsearch.**

clear   calm   perfect   good   clever   expensive

t	g	e	x	p	e	n	s	i	v	e
k	d	x	y	p	e	r	f	e	c	t
c	a	l	m	j	y	c	l	e	a	r
h	x	z	g	o	o	d	m	k	e	p
b	c	l	e	v	e	r	d	a	z	p

2 **Circle the correct *opposite*.**

1 The opposite of a **rough** sea is:

   a a calm sea   **b** an expensive sea

2 The opposite of a **clear** sky is:

   a a perfect sky   **b** a cloudy sky

3 The opposite of a **good** boy is:

   a a clever boy   **b** a bad boy

4 The opposite of a **clever** boy is:

   a an expensive boy   **b** a stupid boy

5 The opposite of an **expensive** boat is:

   a a perfect boat   **b** a cheap boat

Language building

Remember. **Abstract nouns** are the names of thoughts, feelings and qualities.

Daeng said, 'There is no reason for my **fear**.'

1 Underline the *abstract noun* in each sentence.

1 Danger was all around.   **2** Fear showed on his face.

3 He walked slowly in the darkness.

2 Complete these sentences. Use an *abstract noun* from the box.

fear   kindness   anger   danger   darkness

1 A kind person shows _____ .

2 An angry person shows _____ .

3 A frightened person shows _____ .

4 _____ comes when the sun sets.

5 There is _____ when the sea is rough.

3 Use these *abstract nouns* in sentences of your own.

1 sadness

_____

2 happiness

_____

3 goodness

_____

Grammar

1 **Complete the sentences with the verbs in the box.**
Be careful to use the correct forms of the verbs.

> fish   go   crash   be   blow   catch   fall   help

Daeng and Lek _____go_____ fishing every day. Lek _____ Daeng
to pull in the nets. Daeng _____ a good fisherman. He always
_____ lots of fish.
Today Daeng and Lek _____ not _____ . A strong wind
_____ . Heavy rain _____ and huge waves
_____ on the shore.

2 **Write questions for the answers.**

1 _____   Yes, they work hard.
2 What _____   He is helping Daeng.
3 Where _____   They are sitting on the beach.
4 How often _____   They go fishing every day.
5 What _____   He catches fish.
6 _____   Yes, it is raining hard.

3 **Write the sentences again in the negative.**

1 I like swimming.   _____
2 The sun is shining.   _____
3 My uncle lives in Canada.   _____
                             _____
4 We always work hard.   _____
5 The children are watching TV. _____
                             _____
6 I am reading a good book.   _____

4 Look at the pictures and think about the questions.

A Tuesday to Saturday

This is Jenny. What is her job?
Where does she work?
Does she wear a uniform?

B Wednesday

Is Jenny working today?
Is she wearing her uniform?
Who is she looking after?

C Monday to Saturday

This is Toby. What is his job?
Where does he work?
Does he wear a uniform?

D Sunday

Is Toby working today?
Is he wearing his uniform?
What is he doing?

5 Write about Jenny and Toby.

Jenny _____

_____

_____

_____

_____

_____

Toby _____

_____

_____

_____

_____

_____

Spelling

Remember. The suffix **ive** can change a **noun** into an **adjective**.

1 Join the noun and the adjective.

Nouns
1 expense
2 mass
3 secret
4 act

Adjectives
a secretive
b active
c massive
d expensive

1 _____d_____
2 _____
3 _____
4 _____

2 Join the words and meanings.

1 expensive
2 massive
3 secretive
4 active

a doing things
b costs a lot of money
c very big
d not telling

1 _____b_____
2 _____
3 _____
4 _____

3 Use these *ive* words in sentences of your own.

1 expensive

_____

_____

2 massive

_____

_____

Writing

Let's **imagine** that Daeng and Lek caught something in their net which was
• very, VERY heavy
• very, VERY valuable.

1 What do you think it was?

Write your idea here. _____

2 **Write notes.**

Paragraph 1

It was so heavy that Lek had to go into the water to push the net.
He was a very good swimmer.

Think about: Write notes:

What did Lek do when he got into the water?   <u>shivered, gasped</u>

How did he feel?   <u>nervous</u>

How did he get the net onto the boat?   <u>swam down to net,</u>
                                              <u>pushed net up</u>

Paragraph 2

What happened next?   _____

What did Daeng do?   _____

How did he help Lek?   _____

How did he feel?   _____

                                              _____

Paragraph 3

What happened when the net was on the boat?   _____

What was in the net?   _____

What did it look like?   _____

What did Daeng and Lek do?   _____

How did they feel?   _____

What did they say?   _____

Use your notes to **continue the story**.

Paragraph 1
Lek goes into the water.

_____

_____

_____

_____

_____

_____

_____

Paragraph 2
Lek and Daeng get the net out of the water.

_____

_____

_____

_____

_____

_____

Paragraph 3
Lek and Daeng look at what is in the net.

_____

_____

_____

_____

_____

_____

Unit  2

Comprehension

1 Read page 16 again. Match the beginning and ending of each sentence.

1 When water gets warm   **a** by the wind.

2 When water vapour rises   **b** form clouds.

3 When water vapour cools   **c** they fall as rain.

4 These droplets of liquid   **d** it evaporates into water vapour.

5 Clouds are moved   **e** it meets cooler air.

6 When the droplets get big and heavy   **f** it turns back into droplets of liquid.

1   _d_   2 _____

3 _____   4 _____

5 _____   6 _____

2 Read page 17 again. What do the clouds look like in the pictures?

Picture 1 _____

Picture 2 _____

Picture 3 _____

Picture 4 _____

3 What type of weather do these clouds bring?

Picture 1 _____

Picture 2 _____

Picture 3 _____

Picture 4 _____

Vocabulary

Can you find the **missing letters**?

1 The first letter in each pair of words is missing. Use the letters in the box to work out what it is.

> s   c   t   w   r

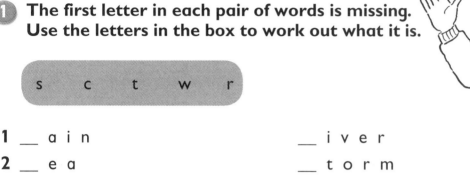

1 __ a i n   __ i v e r

2 __ e a   __ t o r m

3 __ e a t h e r   __ a t e r

4 __ o p   __ a l l

5 __ o o l e r   __ l o u d

2 You have made ten words. Put the words you have made in alphabetical order.

1 _____   2 _____

3 _____   4 _____

5 _____   6 _____

7 _____   8 _____

9 _____   10 _____

3 Use three of the words you have made in sentences of your own.

1 _____

_____

2 _____

_____

3 _____

_____

Language building

Remember. A **phrase** is a group of words which forms part of a sentence. A **phrase** does not make sense on its own.

These clouds look **like cotton wool**.
like cotton wool = **phrase**

1 Some of these are *phrases*. Some of these are sentences.
   Tick the *phrases*.

1 above the land

2 The sun heats up the water.

3 rivers, lakes and the sea

4 as rain

5 into the sky

6 Rain falls from the clouds.

2 Use each of the *phrases* you have ticked in a sentence of your own.

1 _____

_____

2 _____

_____

3 _____

_____

4 _____

_____

Grammar

1 **Complete the sentences with the verbs in the box. Be careful to use the correct forms of the verbs.**

> know   look   be   come   sit   fly   see   think

While the plane __was flying__ over the rainforest, John _____ out of the window. He _____ the trees below him. Monkeys _____ in the branches. Suddenly there _____ a flash of lightning. 'Oh, no!' John _____ . He _____ that a storm _____ .

2 **Make questions for the answers.**
1 Where _____ The plane was flying over the forest.
2 What _____ John saw animals in the trees.
3 What _____ The monkeys were playing.
4 _____ Yes, a storm was coming.
5 How _____ John felt frightened.

3 **Write the sentences again in the negative.**
1 The bird flew slowly. _____
2 It started to snow. _____
3 The sun was shining. _____
4 The animals were sleeping. _____
5 We knew the way. _____
6 I was feeling tired. _____

4 Look at the pictures. Use the words to make a story. Use the correct past tenses.

While – Ben and Tom – walk – forest,

they – see – lots of birds and animals.

Parrots – sit – trees.

Monkeys – swing – branches.

Suddenly – they – hear – roar.

They – turn round – and – see – tiger.

It – hide – trees.

Ben and Tom – stand – still.

While – they – look – it, – tiger – walk away.

'We – lucky,' – say – Bob. – 'tiger – not – hungry!'

5 Now write the story.

<u>While Ben and Tom were walking in the forest,</u>

_____

_____

_____

_____

_____

_____

_____

_____

_____

_____

_____

_____

Spelling

Remember. The letters **tion** sound like **shun**.

1 **Complete the crossword.**

Clues across →

2

4

Clues down ↓

1

3

2 **Choose the best word to complete each sentence.**

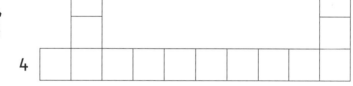

protection   collection   inspection

1 The boy collected stamps for his stamp _____ .

2 You wear a helmet for _____ when you ride a bike.

3 When you look at something carefully, you do an _____ .

3 **Use these 'tion' words in sentences of your own.**

1 station _____

2 action _____

Writing

Look at the pictures. Read the words. They **explain** how a seed grows.

1

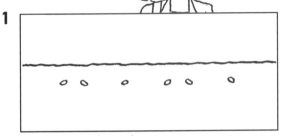

plant, seed, soil

2

roots, grow

3

bigger, suck up, water

4

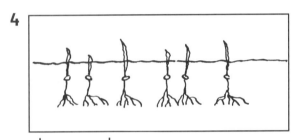

shoot, push up

5

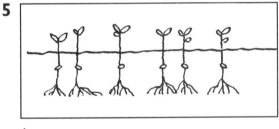

leaves, appear

6

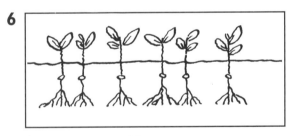

leaves, grow, bigger

7

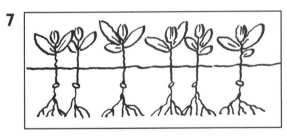

buds, appear

8

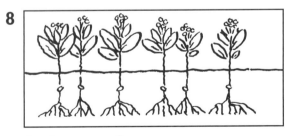

buds, open, flowers

Now use the pictures and the words to **explain** how a seed grows into a plant. Write it in the correct order. Use the **present tense**.

Step 1 _____

_____

Step 2 _____

_____

Step 3 _____

_____

Step 4 _____

_____

Step 5 _____

_____

Step 6 _____

_____

Step 7 _____

_____

Step 8 _____

_____

Unit 3

Comprehension

1 **Read pages 24–25 again. Answer the questions.**
Write *Mum*, *Dad* or *Tim*.

1 Who wanted Tim to go on an adventure holiday? _____
2 Who thought Tim was 'much too young' to go? _____
3 Who went on watching the television? _____
4 Who shouted at Tim? _____
5 Who was good at doing puzzles? _____
6 Who was good at cricket? _____
7 Who gave Tim a cuddle? _____
8 Who bought Tim a safety helmet? _____
9 Who bought Tim new clothes? _____
10 Who hugged Walter Bear? _____

Vocabulary

Remember. We can add to the **beginning** or the **end** of some words to make them longer. We call these words **root words**.
root word = *like*   **dis**like   lik**ing**

1 **Read the words in the wordwall.**

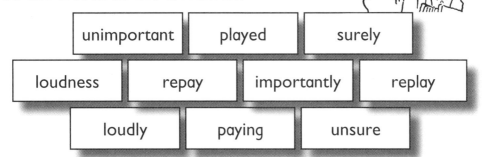

| unimportant | played | surely |

| loudness | repay | importantly | replay |

| loudly | paying | unsure |

2 **Write the pairs of words from the wordwall which come from each *root word*.**

Root word
1 important   _____   _____
2 pay   _____   _____
3 sure   _____   _____
4 loud   _____   _____
5 play   _____   _____

3 **Which words have a *suffix* added at the end?**

1 _____   **2** _____   **3** _____
4 _____   **5** _____   **6** _____

4 **Which words have a *prefix* added at the beginning?**

1 _____   **2** _____
3 _____   **4** _____

Language building

Remember. We use apostrophes
- when a letter or letters are missed out   **didn't** = did not
- for possessive nouns   **Tim's** Dad

1 The apostrophes are missing. Put the apostrophes in the correct places.

1 Tim didn t want to go on an adventure holiday.

2 'Don t shout at him,' said Mum.

3 'You ll love it when you get there,' said Dad.

4 'I ve bought you a safety helmet,' said Mum.

5 'You shouldn t take a teddy bear with you,' said Dad.

2 Use these possessive noun phrases in sentences of your own.

1 the children's holiday _____

_____

2 Tim's drawing _____

_____

3 the girls' adventure _____

_____

4 Dad's favourite sport _____

_____

5 the boy's trainers _____

_____

Grammar

1 **Complete the sentences with the verbs in the boxes.**

> has   have   eaten   ridden   seen   flown   been   heard

1 _____ you ever _____ to Australia?
2 _____ Nina ever _____ a horse?
3 I _____ never _____ that music before.
4 Kim and Ted _____ never _____ the Pyramids.
5 _____ Pat _____ Chinese food before?
6 We _____ _____ to Paris many times.

2 **Billy is talking to Uncle Bob. Complete the sentences.**
Use the correct forms of the verbs in the box.

> see   climb   ride   be   go

Billy: _____ you ever _____ a mountain, Uncle Bob?
Uncle Bob: Yes, I have. I _____ Mount Everest two years ago.
Billy: _____ you ever _____ to a desert?
Uncle Bob: Yes. I _____ _____ to the Gobi Desert.
Billy: When _____ you _____ there?
Uncle Bob: I _____ there in 1998.
Billy: _____ you _____ any interesting animals there?
Uncle Bob: Yes, I did. I _____ yaks and camels.
Billy: _____ you ever _____ a camel?
Uncle Bob: Yes, I have. But I _____ never _____ a yak!

3 Do you remember Ben and Tom, the young explorers? Read the information about them.

Countries visited:
Peru, Mexico (2001), USA, Canada (2002), China, India (2003), Egypt, Morocco (2004), Antarctica (2005).

Main interest:
Animal photography

Photo of the year 2004
1st prize

Books:

Future plans: Next year – Australia!

4 Think about these questions.

1 Have Ben and Tom visited many countries or only a few?

2 When did they go to Mexico? How about India?

3 Do they take photos when they are travelling? What do they like taking photos of?

4 When did they win a photo competition?

5 How many books have they written?

6 What are they going to do next year?

5 Write about Ben and Tom.

_____

_____

_____

_____

_____

_____

_____

_____

Spelling

Remember! Adjectives ending in **ent** can be made into abstract nouns ending in **ence**.

1 **Make the words.**

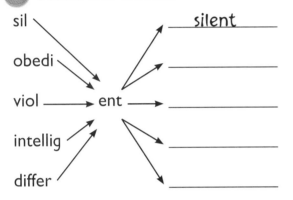

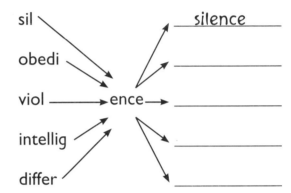

2 **Read the words you have made. Write:**

1 a two syllable word _____

2 a three syllable word _____

3 a four syllable word _____

3 **Use these words in sentences of your own.**

1 silent _____

_____

2 obedience _____

_____

3 intelligent _____

_____

4 difference _____

_____

Writing

Let's write another of Tim's **adventures**.

1 **Write notes.**

- Tim could do these activities:

> abseiling   canoeing   archery   mountain biking

- Which one did you write about in class? _____
- Choose a different activity. _____
- This time, Tim really enjoyed it. He had a great time.
- Remember, you are Tim so write in the first person.

Paragraph 1: How did you feel before the activity?

_____

_____

_____

Paragraph 2: Describe what you did in the activity.

_____

_____

_____

Paragraph 3: Write what you liked about the activity.

_____

_____

_____

Paragraph 4: Write how you felt when you finished.

_____

_____

_____

Now use your notes and write your **adventure** in four paragraphs.

Paragraph 1

_____

_____

_____

_____

_____

Paragraph 2

_____

_____

_____

_____

_____

Paragraph 3

_____

_____

_____

_____

_____

Paragraph 4

_____

_____

_____

_____

_____

Unit

Comprehension

1 Read pages 32–33 again. Write the names of three activities you can do at Woodlands Adventure Park.

1 _____ 2 _____ 3 _____

2 Write the adjective describing:

1 the instructors _____

2 the staff _____

3 the equipment _____

3 Answer the questions.

1 If Sally has a few more lessons, what will she be good at doing?

_____

2 The Green family went out with an instructor. What did the instructor know a lot about?

_____ and _____

3 Why was Tom worried when he went to Woodlands Adventure Park?

_____

4 What three things can you see at the theatre under the trees?

a _____ b _____ c _____

5 Where can you eat at Woodlands Adventure Park? _____

6 Do you have to pay to park your car? _____

7 Which junction on the motorway leads to Woodlands Adventure Park?

_____

8 Which are the two ways you can contact Woodlands Adventure Park?

a _____ b _____

Vocabulary

You have to be careful with words ending in **or** and **er**. Sometimes they sound the same.

1 Find six *or* words in the wordsearch.

d	o	c	t	o	r	h	s	b	u
f	z	e	s	a	i	l	o	r	l
n	t	r	v	i	s	i	t	o	r
i	n	v	e	n	t	o	r	k	d
k	m	b	v	a	c	t	o	r	f
b	a	u	t	h	o	r	d	c	p

2 Write the six *or* words in alphabetical order.

1 _____   2 _____   3 _____

4 _____   5 _____   6 _____

3 Label the pictures with *er* words.

1

2

3

_____   _____   _____

4

5

6

_____   _____   _____

4 Put the labels in alphabetical order.

1 _____   2 _____   3 _____

4 _____   5 _____   6 _____

Language building

> Remember. We can make **adverbs** from adjectives by adding **ly**.
>
> | adjective | adverb |
> |-----------|----------|
> | certain | certainly |
> | true | truly |
> | happy | happily |

1 **Add *ly* to these adjectives to make adverbs. Write the adverbs. Watch your spelling!**

1 slow _____

2 happy _____

3 true _____

4 heavy _____

5 safe _____

6 sad _____

7 lazy _____

8 feeble _____

9 wise _____

10 lucky _____

2 **Use these adverbs in sentences of your own.**

1 correctly _____

_____

2 hungrily _____

_____

3 sensibly _____

_____

4 easily _____

_____

5 bravely _____

_____

Grammar

1 **What will the children do at the adventure park? Look and write. Use the words in the box.**

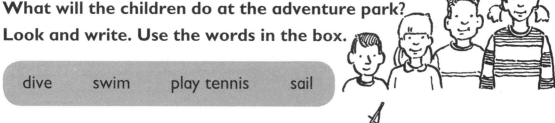

dive	swim	play tennis	sail

1  They _will swim_   2 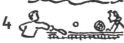 They _____

3 They _____   4 They _____

2 **What new sports will they try? Look and write. Use the words in the box.**

water skiing	mountain biking	canoeing	archery

1 Joe _will try archery._ _____

2 Ellie _____

3 Sam _____

4 Pete _____

3 **Complete the sentences with the correct forms of the verbs.**

1 (have, learn)   If you _____ some archery lessons, you _____
soon _____ .

2 (be, go)   If it _____ very windy, we _____ not _____ sailing.

3 (have, shine)   We _____ a picnic if the sun
_____ .

4 (buy, be)   The children _____ some souvenirs if the shop
_____ not shut.

4 The Carter family are talking about their next summer holiday.

Switzerland is lovely.

Shall we stay at home?

What about the Red Sea?

I'd like to go to Paris.

How about Italy?

Let's go to Egypt!

What will happen if they go to these places?
Choose a picture and a verb from the box.

the Pyramids   the Eiffel Tower   mountains and lakes   diving   pizza   bored

| see | visit | feel | enjoy | eat |

5 **Write.**

If they go to Switzerland, they will _____

_____

_____

_____

_____

What do you think they will do? Why?

_____

What won't they do? Why not?

_____

_____

Spelling

Remember. **Adjectives** ending in **ant** can be made into **abstract nouns** ending in **ance**.

1 Make adjectives and abstract nouns.

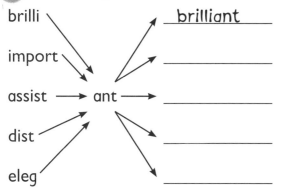

brilli   import   assist ⟶ ant ⟶   dist   eleg

brilliant _____

_____

_____

_____

_____

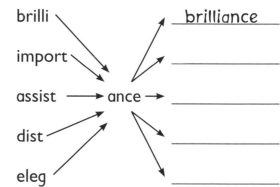

brilli   import   assist ⟶ ance ⟶   dist   eleg

brilliance _____

_____

_____

_____

_____

2 Read the words you have made. Write:

1 a two syllable word   _____

2 a three syllable word   _____

3 Use these words in sentences of your own.

1 brilliance

_____

2 importance

_____

3 assistance

_____

4 distance

_____

5 elegance

_____

Writing

The new attraction at Woodlands Adventure Park is the theatre under the trees. The people who own the park want to give **information** about the theatre and to **persuade** everyone to visit it. They want to put posters in a nearby town. You are going to make a poster for the theatre.

1 **Think of a name for the theatre. Write it here.**

2 **What will people need to know? Make notes.**

What's on	_____
	_____
Opening times	_____
(time, days, dates)	_____
Prices	_____
	_____
How to get there	_____
	_____

3 **What words will you use to persuade people to go?**
Here are some to get you started. Add some more of your own.

wonderful	magical	entertaining	marvellous
_____	_____	_____	_____
_____	_____	_____	_____

4 **What will your poster look like?**

What colours will you use? _____

What illustrations will you use? _____

Now make your **poster**. Use a piece of paper. Make a rough copy first. When you are happy with your poster, do your best copy here.

Check-up 1

1 **Complete the sentences with the verbs in the box. Use present tenses.**

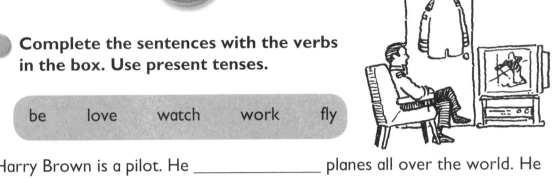

be	love	watch	work	fly

Harry Brown is a pilot. He _____ planes all over the world. He _____ his job. Today he _____ not _____ .
He _____ at home. He _____ TV.

2 **Complete the sentences with the verbs in the box. Use past tenses.**

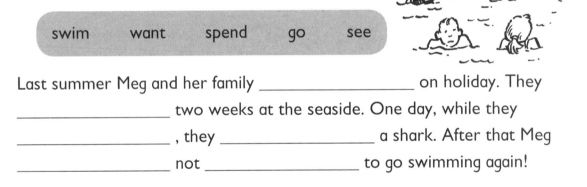

swim	want	spend	go	see

Last summer Meg and her family _____ on holiday. They _____ two weeks at the seaside. One day, while they _____ , they _____ a shark. After that Meg _____ not _____ to go swimming again!

3 **Complete the sentences with *have* or *has* and a verb from the box. Be careful to use the right form of the verb!**

catch	hear	eat	be	see

1 _____ you ever _____ to Italy?
2 I _____ never _____ that music before.
3 Sally _____ never _____ a dolphin.
4 The boys _____ never _____ any fish in this pond.
5 _____ Jim ever _____ Chinese food?

4 What will Sam and Lucy do on holiday? What will they not do? Complete the sentences using the verbs in the box

S ✔ L ✔   S ✗ L ✔   S ✗ L ✗   S ✔ L ✗   S ✗ L ✔

climb   go   ride   swim   play

1 They _____ in the sea.   2 Lucy _____ a horse.

3 Sam _____ water-skiing.   4 They _____ a mountain.

5 Sam _____ basketball.

5 Complete the sentences with the correct forms of the verbs.

1 (be, go)   If the weather _____is_____ fine, we __will go__ for a walk.

2 (rain, stay)   If it _____ , we _____ at home.

3 (pass, work)   Joe _____ his exams if he _____ hard.

4 (feel, eat)   You _____ sick if you _____ all those sweets.

5 (go, learn)   If they _____ to France, they _____ French.

6 Make questions for the answers.

1 _____ ?

No, I have never been to Greece.

2 When _____ ?

Sue went to Spain last year.

3 What _____ ?

He is wearing boots.

4 Where _____ ?

She works at the hospital.

5 _____ ?

Yes, it was raining.

6 How _____ ?

He will travel by plane.

Unit  5

Comprehension

1 **Read pages 42–43 again. Tick the best answer for each question.**

1 Tina's house was

    a large and old. ☐   **b** small and old. ☐   **c** small and new. ☐

2 Mum thought they should

    a open all the boxes at the same time. ☐

    b open the boxes one at a time. ☐

    c put all the boxes in the cupboard. ☐

3 The first box was full of

    a games. ☐   **b** teddy bears. ☐   **c** books. ☐

4 Tina put the books

    a outside. ☐   **b** on the bookshelf. ☐   **c** back in the box. ☐

5 Tina propped the door open with

    a a box. ☐   **b** a chair. ☐   **c** some books. ☐

6 Tina

    a went into the cupboard first. ☐

    b didn't go into cupboard. ☐

    c followed Mum into cupboard. ☐

7 As they crawled further and further into the cupboard, they felt

    a cobwebs. ☐   **b** water. ☐   **c** sand. ☐

8 As they crawled further and further into the cupboard it

    a got darker. ☐   **b** got lighter. ☐   **c** got colder. ☐

Vocabulary

Remember. Words which **sound the same** but have **different meanings** are called **homophones**.

1 Match up the pairs of words which sound the same. Write the words.

1 hole	**a** meet	_____
2 right	**b** pair	_____
3 pear	**c** hair	_____
4 see	**d** whole	_hole/whole_
5 hare	**e** write	_____
6 meat	**f** sea	_____

2 Use these words in sentences of your own.

1 whole

_____

2 right

_____

3 beach

_____

4 beech

_____

5 pair

_____

6 sea

_____

Language building

Remember. We can make **adjectives** from some nouns by adding **y** or **ful**.
noun = powder   adjective = powder**y**
noun = care   adjective = care**ful**

1 **Add y or ful to these nouns to make adjectives. Write the adjectives.**

1 grass _____

2 fear _____

3 pain _____

4 dirt _____

5 sand _____

6 truth _____

7 waste _____

8 silver _____

9 noise _____

10 hope _____

2 **Choose two adjectives from 1 which end in y. Use each one in a sentence of your own.**

1 _____

2 _____

3 **Choose two adjectives from 1 which end in ful. Use each one in a sentence of your own.**

1 _____

2 _____

Grammar

1 **Complete the sentences with *should* or *must*.**

1 You _____ always tell the truth.

2 You _____ write with a pen but a pencil is OK.

3 They _____ watch this TV programme if they have time.

4 You _____ never shout at your parents.

2 **Write questions for these answers.**

1 When _____

She must leave immediately.

2 _____

Yes, you should read this book.

3 What _____

They ought to take an umbrella.

4 How _____

We should travel by plane.

3 **Write these sentences again in the negative.**

1 You must shout.

_____

2 We should run across the street.

_____

3 He ought to go to school.

_____

4 They should climb the mountain.

_____

5 She must travel alone.

_____

4 Look at the picture and answer the questions.

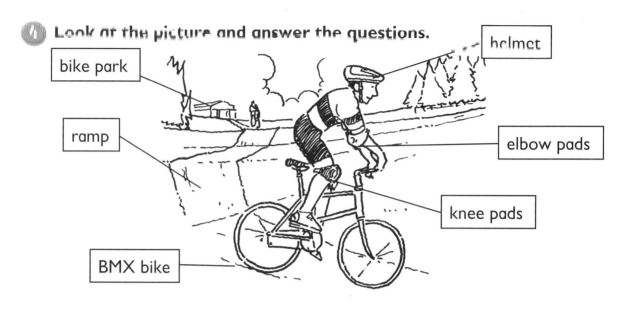

bike park

helmet

ramp

elbow pads

knee pads

BMX bike

1 What kind of bike is this boy riding?

2 If you have a bike like this, should you ride it in the street? Where should you ride it?

3 What should you wear on your elbows?

4 What should you wear on your knees?

5 What must you always wear on your head?

6 If you are a beginner, ought you to try the big ramps?

7 Must you always take care of your bike?

5 Write.

<u>Stay safe at the bike park.</u>

_____

_____

_____

_____

_____

_____

_____

_____

_____

_____

Spelling

Remember. The letters **ture** sound like **cher**.

Captain

1 **Match each word with its meaning.**

1 a hole in a tyre	**a** vulture	**1**	_c_
2 a drawing or painting	**b** furniture	**2**	_____
3 a large bird	**c** puncture	**3**	_____
4 tables, chairs etc	**d** picture	**4**	_____

2 **Find five words ending in *ture*. Write the words.**

a	d	v	e	n	t	u	r	e	k	w
b	i	v	f	r	a	c	t	u	r	e
n	e	g	v	m	i	x	t	u	r	e
t	e	m	p	e	r	a	t	u	r	e
n	d	c	a	p	t	u	r	e	h	m

1 _____   **2** _____

3 _____   **4** _____

5 _____

3 **Use these words in sentences of your own.**

1 mixture

_____

2 vulture

_____

Wrlting

Imagine that you and your Mum or Dad found a **mysterious** cupboard in your new house ...

Which room in your house is the cupboard in? _____

- Why did your Mum or Dad go into the cupboard? Were you looking for something? Were you putting something away? Write your ideas here. ⟶

- What was it like in the cupboard? Think of some interesting adjectives. Write them here. ⟶

- At this point in your story you notice that the floor has changed. You can feel grass and leaves under your feet. Describe what the floor is like. Write your ideas here. ⟶

- What did you see when you walked through the cupboard to the other side? What was it like? Write some words and phrases here. ⟶

Now write the **story** of your **mysterious** cupboard. Continue your story in your copy book if necessary.

Paragraph 1: Why you and your Mum or Dad were looking in the cupboard.

Paragraph 2: Inside the cupboard.

Paragraph 3: How the cupboard changed.

Paragraph 4: On the other side of the cupboard.

_____

_____

_____

_____

_____

_____

_____

_____

_____

_____

_____

_____

_____

_____

_____

_____

_____

_____

_____

Unit

Comprehension

1 **Read pages 50–51 again.**

1 What was Professor Dent talking about?

_____

2 Which ocean was the *Mary Celeste* crossing?

_____

3 On what date was the *Mary Celeste* found 'in the middle of the ocean'?

_____

4 What was the name of the ship which found the *Mary Celeste*?

_____

5 What did the sailors find in the captain's cabin?

_____

6 What did the sailors find in the galley?

_____

7 What does the word 'mutiny' mean?

_____

8 Why do some people think that the captain of the ship was murdered?

_____

9 Does Professor Dent think the mystery will be solved?

_____

10 At the end, what does John Brown ask Professor Dent to do?

_____

2 **If you could ask Professor Dent one question about the *Mary Celeste*, what would you ask him?**

_____

_____

Vocabulary

Remember. If you do not understand a word, use a **dictionary**.

1 **Use these words in sentences of your own.**

1 voyage

_____

2 damaged

_____

3 solved

_____

2 **Here are some more _interesting_ words from the unit. Read them.**

welcome	interesting	masts	Atlantic	happened
called	rowed	discovered	searched	

3 **Which word contains:**

1 cover   _discovered_   **2** as   _____

3 owe   _____   **4** all   _____

5 come   _____   **6** ear   _____

7 rest   _____   **8** ant   _____

9 pen   _____

Language building

Remember. A **simple sentence** has a **subject** and a **verb**.
A simple sentence can also have an **object**.

1 **Write the _subject_, _verb_ and _object_ for each sentence.**

1 Professor Dent talked about the _Mary Celeste_.

Subject = _____

Verb = _____

Object = _____

2 The _Dei Gratia_ found the _Mary Celeste_.

Subject = _____

Verb = _____

Object = _____

3 The sailors found a knife.

Subject = _____

Verb = _____

Object = _____

2 **Think of an object to complete each sentence.**

1 The sailors rowed _____ .

2 The professor wrote _____ .

3 The interviewer asked _____ .

4 The crew left the _____ .

Grammar

1 **Complete the sentences with the words in the boxes.**

is   are   taken   caught   found   grown   made

1 Dolphins _____ _____ in warm seas.

2 Sometimes they _____ _____ in fishermen's nets.

3 This boat _____ _____ of wood.

4 Oranges and lemons _____ _____ in the fields.

5 The fruit _____ _____ to the market in carts.

2 **Write the correct ending.**

by visitors to our country.   by people all over the world.

by shepherds.   by farmers in China.   by travellers in the jungle.

1 Tigers are sometimes seen _____

2 A lot of rice is grown _____

3 Many souvenirs are bought _____

4 Sheep and goats are looked after _____

5 English is spoken _____

3 **Change the sentences.**

1 Many people use mobile phones.

  <u>Mobile phones are used by many people.</u>

2 Most children enjoy cartoons. _____

3 Lots of boys play football. _____

4 Two men sail this ship. _____

5 A chef prepares the meals. _____

4 Look at the pictures and think about the questions.

Troika – Russia

Where are troikas found?

Can you see them in the city or the countryside?

How many horses is a troika pulled by?

Are they used in winter or summer?

Rickshaw – China

Where are rickshaws found?

Can you see them in the city or the countryside?

How many bikes is a rickshaw pulled by?

Are they used all year round?

5 Write about troikas and rickshaws.

_____

_____

_____

_____

_____

_____

_____

_____

_____

_____

_____

_____

Spelling

Remember. Some words have **gu** in them but the **u** is silent.

1 **Choose a word from the box to complete each sentence.**

| guide | guide dog | guess | guitar | guinea pig |

1 Can you _____ the answer to this riddle?
2 I am learning to play the _____ .
3 The _____ took us around the castle.
4 My pet is a _____ _____ .
5 A _____ _____ helps blind people.

2 **In each word the _u_ is missing. Spell each word correctly.**
1 cataloge _____   **2** vage _____
3 disgise _____   **4** gilty _____

3 **Use each of the words you have written in 2 in sentences of your own.**
1 _____
_____
2 _____
_____
3 _____
_____
4 _____
_____

Writing

You are going to write an **interview**.
John Brown is **interviewing** Ben Wilson. Ben has discovered the bones of an unusual dinosaur. Nobody has ever found a dinosaur like this before. He has called it a Whatisitaurus.

1 **Make notes.**

- What will John say at the beginning of the interview?

_____

_____

- Where did Ben find the dinosaur?

_____

- What does it look like?

_____

_____

_____

_____

_____

- How old does he think it is?

_____

_____

- Why is it so unusual?

_____

_____

_____

- What is he going to do with it?

_____

_____

_____

2 **What other questions do you think John will ask? Write your ideas here.**

_____

3 **How will John finish the interview?** _____

_____

4 **Now write the interview.**

Remember. John will **ask** the questions. Ben will **answer** the questions. Set out the **interview** like a play.

Unit

Comprehension

1 **Read pages 58–59 again. Write your answers in sentences.**

1 Why did Daedalus and Icarus go to Crete?

_____

_____

2 Why did the King want a maze?

_____

_____

3 What gave Daedalus the idea to make wings?

_____

_____

4 What did they use to make the wings?

_____

_____

5 What would happen if they flew too near to the sea?

_____

_____

6 What would happen if they flew too near to the sun?

_____

_____

7 Who flew too near to the sun?

_____

_____

8 What happened to his wings?

_____

_____

Vocabulary

All these words are in the story of Daedalus and Icarus.

1 **The letters in these words are jumbled up. Can you sort them out?**

1 l p o b e m r   p _ _ _ _ _ _

2 a e c p e s   e _ _ _ _ _

3 t s i o e d u   o _ _ _ _ _ _

4 d s b r i   b _ _ _ _

5 g h h i   h _ _ _

6 l e t m   m _ _ _

2 **Write the words in alphabetical order.**

1 _____

2 _____

3 _____

4 _____

5 _____

6 _____

3 **Use three of the words in sentences of your own.**

1 _____

_____

2 _____

_____

3 _____

_____

Language building

A **simple sentence** is made up of one main clause.
A **compound sentence** is made up of two simple sentences. The two simple sentences can be joined by the **conjunctions**:
• and   • but   • or

1   **Underline the two *simple* sentences (main clauses) in each *compound* sentence.**

1 Daedalus and Icarus went to Crete and they built the maze.

2 Icarus wanted to go home but Daedalus didn't know what to do.

3 They could climb down the tower or they could fly like the birds.

4 They collected feathers and they made wings.

5 Daedalus did not fly too near the sun but Icarus did fly too high.

2   **Make *compound* sentences from these pairs of *simple* sentences. Use**

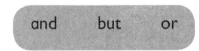

and   but   or

1   The birds were flying. Icarus watched them.

_____

2   Icarus did not know how they could escape. Daedalus had a plan.

_____

3   They could use paper for the wings. They could use feathers.

_____

4   The sun melted the wax. Icarus's wings fell off.

_____

Grammar

1 **Read what the boy says. Then write 'So do I.' or 'Neither do I.'**

1 I like pizza. _____

2 I don't like cold weather. _____

3 I speak English. _____

4 I don't speak Spanish. _____

5 I want to travel when I'm older. _____

2 **Read what the girl says. Then write 'Me too.' Or 'Me neither.'**

1 I love reading. _____

2 I don't have many books. _____

3 I don't walk to school. _____

4 I enjoy sports. _____

5 I watch TV after school. _____

3 **Find the correct responses in the box and write.**

> So is my sister.   So do girls.   So did my uncle.
> So does Lucy's.   Neither can Harry.

1 John can't drive. _____

2 Pat went to Mexico last summer. _____

3 My brother is good at swimming. _____

4 Kate's father works abroad. _____

5 Boys enjoy basketball. _____

4 Read these details about Jenny.

2001 – 2003: lived at the seaside.
Now lives in the city near the park.

One brother, two sisters.

Likes: music; plays the guitar
Dislikes: sport

5 Jenny is talking to a new girl at school. Her name is Holly.
Complete their conversation.

Jenny: _____ before you came here, Holly?

Holly: I lived at the seaside.

Jenny: Really? _____ now?

Holly: I live near the park.

Jenny: Oh! _____ !
_____ ?

Holly: Yes, I have. I've got one brother and two sisters.

Jenny: I don't believe it! _____ !
_____ ?

Holly: I don't like sports very much.

Jenny: _____ !

Holly: But I love music. I can play the guitar.

Jenny: _____ !
I think we're going to be good friends.

Holly: _____ !

Spelling

Remember. The letters **ie** in some words sound like **ee**.

1 **Find five *ie* words in the wordsearch.**

n	r	d	p	i	e	c	e	k	j
f	i	e	l	d	j	c	x	w	q
j	t	s	h	i	e	l	d	b	k
b	j	h	y	r	c	h	i	e	f
b	g	t	h	i	e	f	d	s	o

2 **Write the correct word under each picture.**

1

2

3

_____ _____ _____

4

5

_____ _____

3 **Use some of the *ie* words in sentences of your own.**

_____

_____

_____

Writing

Now you will write **Scene 4** of the play. Remember that Daedalus has found out where his son is. He hurries off to find him.

• **Look carefully at the picture which shows you Scene 4.**

• **Make notes.**

Who are the **characters** in Scene 4? _____

_____

Write some nouns and adjectives _____

to describe the **setting**. _____

What does Daedalus **say** when _____

he first sees Icarus? _____

What does he do? What **stage** _____

direction will you write? _____

What does Icarus **say** when he _____

first sees Daedalus? _____

What does he do? What **stage** _____

direction will you write? _____

How is Daedalus feeling? _____

_____

How is Icarus feeling? _____

_____

What do they do at the end _____

of the scene? _____

- **Now write the scene.**

Remember to write:
- the characters' names
- what they say
- what they do (stage directions)

Narrator: Daedalus has found out where his son is. He hurries off to find him.

_____   _____

_____   _____

_____

_____   _____

_____

_____   _____

_____

_____   _____

_____

_____   _____

_____

_____   _____

_____

Unit 8

Comprehension

1 **Read pages 66–67 again. Find these facts.**

1 The names of the three astronauts.

a _____

b _____

c _____

2 The date and time when the astronauts landed on the Moon.

Date _____   Time _____

3 The name of the spacecraft which took the astronauts to the Moon.

_____

4 The name of the spacecraft which landed on the Moon.

_____

5 The name of the first astronaut to walk on the Moon.

_____

6 The name of the second astronaut to walk on the Moon.

_____

7 What three things the astronauts took photographs of.

a _____

b _____

c _____

8 What the astronauts collected.

_____ and _____

9 How long the astronauts walked on the Moon.

_____

10 How far away the Moon is from Earth.

_____

Vocabulary

Remember. A **synonym** is a word that means **the same** or **nearly the same** as another word. An **antonym** means the **opposite** of a word.

1 **Replace the underlined words with a *synonym*.**

1 The journey to the Moon was <u>amazing</u>.

_____

2 The Eagle spacecraft was <u>tiny</u>.

_____

3 The journey down to the Moon's surface was <u>hazardous</u>.

_____

4 The astronaut said he had made a <u>giant</u> leap for mankind.

_____

5 Neil Armstrong walked very <u>carefully</u>.

_____

6 They used buckets and spades to <u>collect</u> dust and rocks.

_____

2 **Match each word with its opposite.**

1 amazing   **a** big
2 tiny   **b** carelessly
3 hazardous   **c** dull
4 carefully   **d** small
5 giant   **e** easy

1 <u>dull</u>   **2** _____
3 _____   **4** _____
5 _____

Language building

Remember. When we add words like **off**, **up, back** to verbs they are called **phrasal verbs**. They often change the meaning of the verb.

verb = climb   phrasal verb = climb down

1 **Copy the sentences. Use a *phrasal verb* from the box instead of the underlined words.**

> speed up   broke down   came back   put it off   got rid of

1 I had homework to do but I <u>did it later</u>.

_____

2 The clock <u>stopped working</u>.

_____

3 I <u>threw away</u> my old toys.

_____

4 I had to <u>go more quickly</u> because I was late for school.

_____

5 I <u>returned</u> home at six o'clock.

_____

2 **Use these *phrasal verbs* in sentences of your own.**

1 got up _____

_____

2 came in _____

Grammar

1 **What are the Watsons doing this week? Put the words in the right order.**

1 playing Tuesday. match in is football a Joe on

_____

2 cousin's staying on are house children Friday their night. The at

_____

3 Watson going a Mr on Tuesday trip. On is business

_____

4 is to morning. flying in He the Paris early

_____

5 Watson having lesson. Mrs driving On a Wednesday is

_____

6 driving is her She test Thursday. taking on

_____

2 **What are these children doing at the weekend? Use the verbs in brackets.**

1 _____ (buy)

2 _____ (go)

3 _____ (get)

4 _____ (play)

3 Look at the message board in the Watson family's kitchen.

Monday – Grandma – train arrives 4.30

Joe and Meg – School closed on Thursday

DON'T FORGET!! Basketball competition Friday – 3.00pm Please come! Meg

Dad's fishing trip!!
Leave: Saturday a.m.
Return (with huge fish!):
Sunday p.m.

Cousin Lucy's surprise party – Wednesday 8.30 All invited!!

Mum – the dentist phoned. He's changed your appointment from Thurs. 10.00 to Fri. 9.30

Friday – NEW CAR!

JOE! Guitar lesson 5.30 Tuesday

4 What are the Watsons doing this week? Write their plans in order. Start with Monday.

On Monday _____

_____

_____

_____

_____

_____

_____

_____

_____

_____

_____

_____

_____

_____

_____

_____

_____

_____

_____

Spelling

Remember **ei** can make the sound **ay**.

1 **Do the crossword.**

Clues across →

5 ⟨18⟩

6 ⟨80⟩

Clues down↓

1

2 ⟨8⟩

3

4

2 **Do these words have *ie* or *ei*? Finish the words.**

1 s h __ __ l d

2 __ __ g h t

3 p __ __ c e

4  v __ __ n

5 r __ __ n s

6  f __ __ l d

Writing

Read the **notes** about the first American to orbit the earth.

Name:	John Glenn
Age:	41 years old
Nationality:	American
Date of space flight:	February 20th, 1962
Launch site:	Cape Canaveral
Name of spacecraft:	Friendship 7
What he did:	Orbited the Earth three times.
What he said:	'The sky in space is very black with a thin band of blue along the horizon.'
Speed of orbit:	281,627.5 kilometres per hour
Time in space:	4 hours 55 minutes
How he landed:	Inside the space craft. Splashed down in the sea.

Use the notes to write a newspaper report about the first American to orbit the Earth. Write your ideas here.

1 Ideas for the headline.

2 Ideas for the opening paragraph.

3 Ideas for the illustration.

Write your **newspaper report**.

headline

byline

illustration

opening paragraph

the rest of the report

Unit  9

Comprehension

Read page 75 again. Answer the questions.

Moonlight

1 Find and write four adjectives which describe the moon.

a _____   b _____

c _____   d _____

2 What time is it in the poem?   _____

Spaceflight

3 Where is the spaceship going?   _____

4 Is 'blasting off' the beginning or the end of the journey? _____

Stars

5 The poet uses two phrases to describe the stars.
What are the phrases?

a _____

b _____

6 Find and write the two adjectives which describe the sun.

a _____   b _____

7 Which haiku do you like best? Explain your reasons.

_____

_____

_____

_____

Vocabulary

Remember. Some words have **more than one meaning**.

1 Use these *verbs* in sentences of your own.

1 plant _____

_____

2 watch _____

_____

2 Use these *nouns* in sentences of your own.

1 orange _____

_____

2 plant _____

_____

3 watch _____

_____

4 sound _____

_____

3 Use these *adjectives* in sentences of your own.

1 sound _____

_____

2 orange _____

_____

Language building

Remember. We can use some **ing** verbs as **adjectives**.
The moon is **shining**. Watch the **shining** moon

ing verb   **ing** adjective

1 Change the verbs to *ing* adjectives.

Verb	*ing* adjective
1 to run	the _____ boy
2 to smile	the _____ teacher
3 to cry	the _____ baby
4 to flow	the _____ river
5 to sing	the _____ bird
6 to flower	the _____ plant
7 to jump	the _____ frog
8 to sparkle	the _____ ring

2 Use these *ing* adjectives in sentences of your own.

1 glowing _____

_____

2 laughing _____

_____

3 roaring _____

_____

Grammar

1 **Make sentences with *so*.**

1 tall The giraffe is so tall! _____

2 fierce _____

3 funny _____

4 sweet _____

5 strong _____

2 **Complete the sentences with *such a*, *such an* or *such*.**

1 We watched _____ exciting match!

2 Our team had _____ good players!

3 Those boys are _____ fast runners!

4 My grandmother is _____ kind person!

3 **Complete the sentences with words from the boxes.**

| so such a such an such | interesting strong boring greedy hungry |

1 It's _____ _____ book that I've read it three times.

2 The children were _____ _____ that they ate all the biscuits.

3 They were _____ _____ children that they finished the cakes, too.

4 It was _____ _____ film that I fell asleep.

5 The wind was _____ _____ that it blew down trees.

4 **Look at the pictures and think about the questions.**

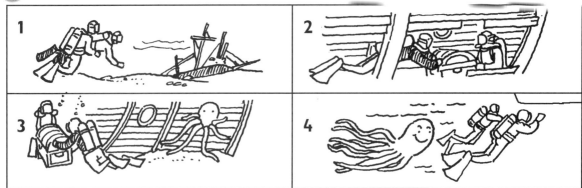

1 Look at picture 1. Where were Gus and Fred diving? Was the water clear or cloudy? What did they see?

2 Look at picture 2. Did they swim inside the wreck? Did they find a shark or a chest? Was it new or old? Could they open it?

3 Look at picture 3. Was the chest heavy or light? Could they lift it? What did they see suddenly?

4 Look at picture 4. Was the octopus tiny or huge? How did Gus and Fred feel? Did they swim into a cave or up to their boat?

Write the story. Try to include the words in the box.

so clear that	such an old chest that
so heavy that	such a huge octopus that

_____

_____

_____

_____

_____

_____

_____

_____

Spelling

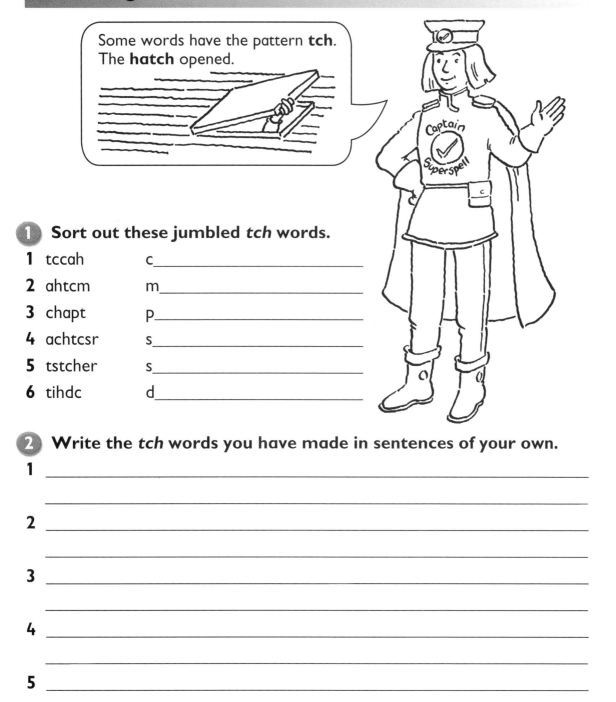

Some words have the pattern **tch**.
The **hatch** opened.

1 Sort out these jumbled *tch* words.

1 tccah   c_____

2 ahtcm   m_____

3 chapt   p_____

4 achtcsr   s_____

5 tstcher   s_____

6 tihdc   d_____

2 Write the *tch* words you have made in sentences of your own.

1 _____

_____

2 _____

_____

3 _____

_____

4 _____

_____

5 _____

_____

6 _____

_____

Writing

1 **Haikus can be about anything. Here are some titles for haikus.**

Dinosaurs	Trees	The sea

2 **Here are some adjectives you can use in these haikus.**
Write them under the title where you think they fit the best.

beautiful   blue   green   leafy

pounding   gigantic   foamy   roaring

endless   dangerous   wonderful   fierce

3 **Now sort the adjectives into lists.**

1 One syllable	2 Two syllables	3 Three syllables

4 Can you finish this haiku? Write a syllable on each line.

Dinosaurs

Din o saurs _____ _____
Dan ger ous and _____ _____ _____
They _____ _____ _____ _____

5 Now write your own haiku about trees or the sea:

_____ title

_____ _____ _____ _____ _____ 5 syllables

_____ _____ _____ _____ _____ _____ _____ 7 syllables

_____ _____ _____ _____ _____ 5 syllables

6 Draw a picture to illustrate your haiku.

Check-up 2

1 **Complete the answers to the questions.**

1 Jenny has a toothache. What should she do?

_____ to the dentist.

2 It is wrong to tell a lie. What must we always do?

_____ the truth.

3 Tom is always late for school. What ought he to do?

_____ home earlier.

2 **Complete the sentences with the words in the boxes.**

| is | are | | seen | made | used | grown |

1 These toys _____ _____ of wood.
2 Rice _____ _____ in India.
3 Sometimes a tiger _____ _____ in this forest.
4 Horses and donkeys _____ _____ for transport.

3 **Change the sentences.**

1 Both boys and girls play basketball.

<u>Basketball is played by both boys and girls.</u>_____

2 Hundreds of people visit the zoo.

_____

3 Tourists buy souvenirs.

_____

4 All the staff speak English.

_____

5 Everyone enjoys these films.

_____

4 **Billy agrees with Lisa. Write 'So do I' or 'Neither do I'.**

Lisa   Billy

1 I like chocolate. _____

2 I don't speak French. _____

3 I want to learn the guitar. _____

4 I don't have any sisters. _____

5 **What are these children doing next week?**
Use the verbs in the box.

> visit   get   go   have   play

1 Jane – singing lesson – Monday _Jane is having a singing lesson_
on Monday.

2 Tom – tennis – Thursday _____

3 Kim and Joe – grandma – Sunday _____

4 Sally – shopping – Saturday _____

5 Sam and Meg – puppy – Tuesday _____

6 **Complete the sentences with *so*, *such a*, *such an* or *such*.**

1 I am reading _____ interesting book!

2 The weather is _____ hot in August!

3 Our baker makes _____ delicious cakes!

4 James can run _____ fast!

5 There is _____ good programme on TV tonight!

1 **Read pages 84–85 again. Number each sentence in order.**

	Jim dived in the sea and swam to the island.
	The rocks tore a hole in the side of the ship.
1	Enormous waves threw the ship onto the rocks.
	When he reached the island, Jim went straight to sleep.
	Jim drank some fresh water and ate some coconut.
	The captain shouted, 'Swim for your life!'
	Jim found a map of the island in a leather case.
	He built a shelter with wood, branches and leaves.

Vocabulary

1 Find seven words from the story.

q	w	r	t	y	p	a	n	i	c	p	l	k	j	h
z	x	s	t	a	g	g	e	r	e	d	m	n	b	v
c	v	g	f	r	t	e	x	h	a	u	s	t	e	d
b	m	y	s	t	e	r	i	o	u	s	t	r	f	g
w	q	p	s	h	i	v	e	r	i	n	g	s	a	z
m	n	s	u	r	v	i	v	o	r	p	w	q	r	a
x	e	x	p	l	o	r	e	r	r	w	q	t	s	y

2 Match each word with its meaning. *Use the dictionary to help you.*

1 panic   **a** very tired
2 staggered   **b** shaking because you are cold or frightened
3 exhausted   **c** a feeling of fear and you can't think clearly
4 mysterious   **d** someone who is still alive
5 shivering   **e** someone who travels to new places to find out about them
6 survivor   **f** very strange
7 explorer   **g** walked and nearly fell over

1 panic - a feeling of fear and you can't think clearly
2 _____
3 _____
4 _____
5 _____
6 _____
7 _____

Language building

Remember! In direct speech the **reporting clause** (the words that tell you who is speaking) can come at the (a) **beginning**, (b) **middle** or (c) **end of the sentence**.

a *The sailor screamed*, 'Get out of my way. I want to get off this ship!

b 'Get out of my way,' *the sailor screamed*. 'I want to get off this ship!'

c 'Get out of my way. I want to get off this ship!' *the sailor screamed*.

1 **Rewrite each sentence with the reporting clause at the end.**

1 The captain shouted, 'Abandon ship!'

'Abandon ship!' the captain shouted.

2 The pirate exclaimed, 'I can see an island!'

_____

3 Jim whispered, 'Come quietly and don't make a sound.'

_____

2 **Rewrite each sentence with the reporting clause at the beginning.**

1 'Your dinner is ready. Come and eat it,' the cook cried.

_____

2 'Look at the big waves. I think a storm is coming,' a sailor said.

_____

3 'The ship is sinking! Swim for your life!' the captain shouted.

_____

3 **Now rewrite the sentences in 2 again. Put the reporting clause in the middle of each sentence.**

1 _____

2 _____

3 _____

Grammar

1 **Complete the speech bubbles.**

1 Tom said that he was feeling hungry.

2 Lucy said that the cakes were delicious.

3 Maggie said that she could not find her glasses.

4 Paul said that he had not got his homework.

5 Sue said that she liked funny films.

2 **Change the verbs.**

1 'I am tired.'   Karen said that she _____ tired.

2 'I can hear an owl.'   Billy said that he _____ an owl.

3 'I have got a headache.' Joe said that he _____ a headache.

4 'I love my new kitten.' Molly said that she _____ her new kitten.

5 'Snow is falling.'   Sam said that snow _____ .

3 **What did they say?**

1 'I can see an eagle.'
  Mark said that _____

2 'I like singing.'
  Susie said that _____

3 'It is raining.'
  Mum said that _____

4 'I have got a new bike.'
  Dan said that _____

4 Look at the pictures. Write notes to answer the questions.

1 Look at picture 1. Where were Daisy and Jack going? Was the sky blue or grey? What did Daisy say?

2 Look at picture 2. Did the clouds get darker and darker or lighter and lighter? What did Jack say?

3 Look at picture 3. Did the rain get heavier? What did Daisy say?

4 Look at picture 4. Suddenly what came out from behind a cloud? What did Jack say?

5 Write the story.

_____

_____

_____

_____

_____

_____

_____

Spelling

This word is broken into two **syllables**. The first **syllable** ends with a **long vowel**.

o / pen
The chest is open.

1 Divide each word into two syllables.

1 shi / ning   **2** broken   **3** open

4 baby   **5** spider   **6** student

7 Egypt   **8** police   **9** tiger

10 quiet   **11** April   **12** paper

2 Finish each word with its second syllable.

1 po + _lice_ = _police_   **2** bro + _____ = _____

3 stu + _____ = _____   **4** A + _____ = _____

5 ti + _____ = _____   **6** E + _____ = _____

7 o + _____ = _____   **8** qui + _____ = _____

9 spi + _____ = _____   **10** pa + _____ = _____

11 ba + _____ = _____   **12** shi + _____ = _____

3 Write the twelve words in alphabetical order.

1 _____   **2** _____   **3** _____

4 _____   **5** _____   **6** _____

7 _____   **8** _____   **9** _____

10 _____   **11** _____   **12** _____

Writing

Think about Chapter 5 of the story. Look at the map on page 85 of your book. Choose the place you think Jim explored next.

Write some notes.

- What did Jim see when he reached the place?
- What did he think?
- How did he feel?   **?**

Beginning

- Something exciting happened. What was it?
- What did Jim do? What did he think? How did he feel?   **?**

Middle

- What happened at the end? Was Jim hurt? Did he escape?   **?**

End

Use your notes to help you write Chapter 5 of the story. First think of a good title for the chapter! Next, write your chapter in three separate paragraphs (one about the beginning, one about the middle and one about the end of the adventure.) Finish your chapter in your copy book if you do not have enough space.

Chapter 5 _____

_____

_____

_____

_____

_____

_____

_____

_____

_____

_____

_____

_____

_____

_____

_____

_____

_____

_____

_____

_____

_____

_____

_____

_____

Unit  11

Comprehension

1 **Read pages 92–93 again. Match up the beginning of each sentence with its correct ending.**

1 Greece covers   [c]

2 Greece has a population of   [ ]

3 Athens is   [ ]

4 Crete is   [ ]

5 In the south there are   [ ]

6 It is very mountainous   [ ]

7 Fishing, farming and tourism are   [ ]

8 The Acropolis in Athens was   [ ]

9 The Minotaur was the name of   [ ]

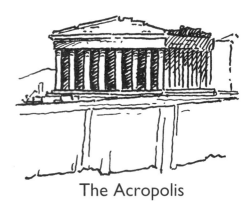

The Acropolis

a the capital of Greece.

b the largest island.

c over 130,000 square kilometres.

d in the north of Greece.

e a meeting place for important people.

f more than ten million people.

g a monster.

h the main industries.

i plains and forests.

The Minotaur

Vocabulary

Check the spellings on pages 160–165.

1 **Complete these words from Unit 11 correctly.**

1 industr __ __ s

2 landsc __ p __

3 h __ __ dings

4 rep __ __ t

5 loca __ __ __ __

6 popula __ __ __ __

7 civilisa __ __ __ __

2 **Use the words correctly in these sentences.**

1 Ben wrote a _____ on Greece.

2 Ben wrote his notes under different _____ .

3 The _____ of Greece is south east Europe.

4 Greece has a _____ of over ten million people.

5 The _____ in the north of Greece is very mountainous.

6 The main _____ of Greece are tourism, farming and fishing.

7 Greek _____ is over four thousand years old.

3 **Here are some more words from the unit.**

| countries | information | square | language | capital |
| island | forest | farming | legend |

Which word contains:

1 land? _____

2 age? _____

3 form? _____

4 arm? _____

5 are? _____

6 rest? _____

7 cap? _____

8 end? _____

9 tries? _____

Language building

Remember! We can write a **sentence** as **question**, a **statement** or an **exclamation**.

When was the Acropolis built?   (question)

It was built 2,500 years ago.   (statement)

That's amazing!   (exclamation)

1 **Punctuate each sentence correctly. Say if it is a statement** **S** **, question** **Q** **or exclamation** **E** **.**

1 What a lovely surprise to see you _____   ☐

2 There are many beautiful beaches in Greece _____   ☐

3 Do you know where Greece is _____   ☐

4 How far can you swim _____   ☐

5 I like swimming in the sea _____   ☐

6 Get out of my way at once _____   ☐

2 **Each statement is the answer to a question. Write a sensible question to go with each statement.**

1 _____

The main language of Greece is Greek.

2 _____

Athens is in the south of Greece.

3 _____

This Greek coin is two thousand years old.

4 _____

Sappho, the Greek poet, lived 2,500 years ago.

5 _____

Farmers put sheets under the trees to catch the olives when they fall.

Grammar

1 **Complete the sentences with the words in the boxes.**

> was   were

> used   found   built   destroyed   held

1 A stadium _____ _____ in Athens 2000 years ago.
2 It _____ _____ for sports by the ancient Greeks.
3 In 2004 the Olympic Games _____ _____ in Athens.
4 Strange pictures _____ _____ in the Nazca desert.
5 The town of Pompeii _____ _____ by a volcanic eruption.

2 **Make sentences.**

1 valuable museum. painting Yesterday was from a stolen city the

_____

2 woman. was a and It by taken a man

_____

3 staff. the were museum Luckily thieves by seen

_____

4 were police. soon by They the caught

_____

3 **Change the sentences.**

1 Someone broke the window.   <u>The window was broken.</u>
2 Someone stole my camera.   _____
3 People found pictures in the caves.   _____
4 People saw sharks near the beach.

_____

5 Someone took money from her bag.

_____

4 **Look at the picture and read the notes.**

Old London Bridge
the River Thames
started: 1176
completed: about 20 years later
houses and shops
1666 Great Fire of London
many buildings burnt down
bridge saved
1820 old bridge pulled down
new bridge built

5 **Think about these questions.**

1 Which river was Old London Bridge built across?

2 When was it started and when was it finished?

3 What were built on the bridge?

4 What happened in London in 1666?

5 Were many buildings burnt down? Was the bridge destroyed?

6 What happened to the old bridge? Was a new bridge built across the river?

6 **Write about Old London Bridge.**

_____
_____
_____
_____
_____
_____
_____
_____
_____
_____
_____

Spelling

Remember. In some words the letters **ci** and **ti** sound like **sh**.

My food is deli**ci**ous.

1 **Choose ci or ti to complete each word.**

1 deli___ous

2 loca___on

3 an___ent

4 pre___ous

5 pa___ent

6 popula___on

7 ini___al

8 spe___al

9 musi___an

10 cau___ous

2 **Read the definitions. Use each word from 1.**

1 very old [a][n][c][i][e][n][t]

2 first

3 someone who plays music

4 careful

5 tastes very nice

6 the number of people who live in a place

7 very valuable

8 the place where something is

9 can wait for a long time and not get angry

10 different from anyone or anything

Writing

Finish these notes I wrote about Egypt. Use the notes on page 92 to help you.

Introduction Location _____ North East Africa.

S_____ Over 1,000,000 square kilometres

P_____ Over 60 million

M_____ L_____ Arabic

C_____ C_____ Cairo.

L_____ River Nile (6670 k_____ long) runs through middle of country.

Land on both sides of Nile good for farming.

95% of Egypt – sandy desert.

Highest m_____ – Jabal Katrinah (2,637 m_____ high)

M_____ I_____ Cotton (for clothes)
Oil
Suez Canal (for shipping)
Tourism

H_____ Ancient Egyptian c_____ – about 5000 years old
Historic sites to visit include:
The Pyramids at Giza, near Cairo
The Valley of Kings at Luxor
Abu Simbul (two famous temples built by Ramses 11).

Use my notes opposite and write a report about Egypt.

- Use the report on page 93 to help you.
- Write the information in four paragraphs.
- Give each paragraph a heading.
- Find out some more about Egypt if you can.
- Write an extra paragraph at the end called 'More information'.
- Write some interesting sentences about what you have discovered.

Report on Egypt by _____

_____

_____

_____

_____

_____

_____

_____

_____

_____

_____

_____

_____

_____

_____

_____

_____

_____

_____

_____

Continue your report in your copy book if you need more space.

Unit  Comprehension

1 **Read pages 100–101 again. Answer the questions.**

1 What was wrong with the water in the stream?

_____

2 What job did Kofi do every morning?

_____

3 Who did Kofi see on a donkey cart?

_____

4 What was Old Man Awam's job?

_____

5 What did the old man do when Kofi waved to him?

_____

_____

6 Why did Kofi go to the tannery?

_____

_____

7 Why did Kofi hide behind a bush?

_____

_____

8 What did Kofi see?

_____

_____

Vocabulary

Use the thesaurus on page 166 of Language Book 5 to help you.

1 Which word in the unit means the same as:

1 glared   f_____

2 irritable   b_____

3 unclean   p_____

4 muttering m_____

5 bring   f_____

6 fluid   l_____

7 dark   g_____

8 fighting   s_____

2 Match up each word with its opposite.

1 polluted   [e]   **a** take

2 fetch   [ ]   **b** giving in

3 frowned   [ ]   **c** bright

4 struggling   [ ]   **d** solid

5 bad-tempered [ ]   **e** clean

6 gloomy   [ ]   **f** shouting

7 mumbling   [ ]   **g** good-tempered

8 liquid   [ ]   **h** smiled

Language building

Remember. The **future tense** tells you what will happen in the future.

I **will collect** some water tomorrow.

1 **What do you think will happen tomorrow? Answer the questions.**

1 What day will it be tomorrow?

_____

2 What will the weather be like?

_____

3 What time will you get up?

_____

4 What will you wear?

_____

5 What will you eat for breakfast?

_____

6 Where will you go?

_____

7 What will the traffic be like on the roads?

_____

8 What will your mother say to you?

_____

9 What will be on TV?

_____

10 What nice thing will happen to you?

_____

Grammar

1 **Complete the sentences with words from the boxes.**

has have	taught flown been played lived

1 Mr and Mrs Harvey _____ _____ in their house for thirty years.

2 Miss Parker _____ _____ at the school since September.

3 Joe _____ _____ in hospital since Monday.

4 Lucy and Sam _____ _____ the piano since they were five.

5 Bill and Bob _____ _____ planes for years.

2 **Complete the sentences with *for* or *since*.**

1 She has worked as a dentist _____ 1998.

2 He has grown wheat on his farm _____ many years.

3 They have lived in their house _____ last March.

4 Polly has been ill _____ Tuesday.

5 I haven't seen Eddie _____ a long time.

3 **Look, read and write sentences.**

1

have – dog – ten years

He has had a dog for ten years.

2

work – nurse – eighteen months

_____

3

live – house – 1980

_____

4 Look at the pictures and read.

'I've lived in this town all my life. I opened the toy shop two years ago. I've sold hundreds of toys since then. Last year I started to sell computer games, too.'

'We arrived in the town in 2003. We opened the sweet shop one year later. We started to make ice cream last summer. Hundreds of children have bought our ice cream. It's delicious!'

5 Think about these questions.

1 How long has Mr Jolly lived in the town? How long has he had his toyshop?
2 How many toys has he sold? How long has he sold computer games?
3 How long have Mr and Mrs Tubb lived in the town?
4 How long have they had their sweet shop?
5 How long have they made ice cream? How many children have bought their ice cream?

6 Write about Mr Jolly and Mr and Mrs Tubb.

_____

_____

_____

_____

_____

_____

_____

_____

_____

_____

_____

Spelling

Remember. Sometimes **different letter patterns** can make the **same sound**.
a str**ea**m   a st**ee**p hill

1 **Choose the correct letters to complete each word.**

1 str __ __ m   (ea / ee)
2 d __ __ n   (ou / ow)
3 sch __ __ l   (ew / oo)
4 pl __ __   (ai / ay)
5 n __ __ vous   (er / ir)
6 sh __ __ ts   (au / or)
7 st __ __ p   (ea / ee)
8 cl __ __ d   (ou / ow)
9 kn __ __   (ew / oo)
10 cont __ __ ners   (ai / ay)
11 t __ __ n   (ir / ur)
12 sh __ __ t   (ir / ur)
13 exh __ __ sted   (au / aw)
14 __ __ ful   (au / aw)

2 **Choose a word from above that rhymes with:**

1 town – _____   6 away – _____
2 burn – _____   7 deep – _____
3 sports – _____   8 loud – _____
4 dream – _____   9 drew – _____
5 pool – _____   10 skirt – _____

Spelling: words containing same sounds but different letter patterns 99

Writing

Use these words to label the picture.

Old Man Awam   Kofi   bush   forest
tannery   polluted water   river
oil drum   horse and cart   animal skins

Write a description of the picture opposite. Use my questions to help you. Continue your description in your copy book.

1 What time of day is it?
2 Where is Old Man Awam?
3 What is he holding?
4 What is he tipping into the river?
5 Where is Kofi?
6 What is he doing?
7 How does he look?
8 Where is the tannery?
9 What can you see outside the tannery?
10 What sounds can you hear from:
   a the river?   b the water from the oil drum?   c the forest?
11 What can you smell?

Unit  13

Comprehension

1 Read pages 108–109 again. Choose the correct answer for each gap.

1 Our forests are _____ (unclean, disappearing).

2 Our air and water are _____ (extinct, unclean).

3 There is _____ (pollution, water) everywhere.

4 World Watch has:

   a asked governments to pass laws about _____ (wildlife, pollution).

   b encouraged people to _____ (clean, recycle) materials.

   c prevented _____ (traffic pollution, oil spills) at sea.

   d protected the world's _____ (wildlife, factories).

5 When you join World Watch you will receive:

   a an _____ (leaflet, information pack) about our work.

   b a 'Save the World' _____ (poster, watch).

   c a monthly World Watch _____ (project, magazine).

6 World Watch promises to spend every _____ (penny, pound) you give to make the world a _____ (good, better) place.

Vocabulary

1 The first letter in each set of words is missing. Work out what it is.

The same letter is missing in each set of words. Each of the words comes from Unit 13.

1 __owerful	__ersuade	__rotected	__ollution
2 __orests	__uture	__orward	__actories
3 __ords	__orld	__ildlife	__atch
4 __sked	__tmosphere	__dvice	__nimals
5 __emind	__educed	__ecycle	__egular
6 __an	__ities	__ounts	__ompetitions

2 Now write each set of words in alphabetical order.

1 _____ _____ _____ _____

2 _____ _____ _____ _____

3 _____ _____ _____ _____

4 _____ _____ _____ _____

5 _____ _____ _____ _____

6 _____ _____ _____ _____

Language building

A **verb** can be:

a) **active**

(subject)   (verb)   (object)

The man   wrote   a leaflet.

The subject (the man) did something (wrote) to something (a leaflet).

b) **passive**

(object)   (verb)   (subject)

The leaflet   was written   by the man.

The object (a leaflet) has something done to it (was written) by the subject (the man).

1 **Underline the subject and object in each sentence. Circle the active verb.**

1 The <u>children</u> (carried) <u>containers</u> of water.

2 The girl turned on the tap.

3 The elephant drank some water.

2 **Underline the subject and object in each sentence. Circle the passive verb.**

1 Containers of water were carried by the children.

2 The tap was turned on by the girl.

3 Some water was drunk by the elephant.

3 **Rewrite each sentence. Change the verb from the passive to the active.**

1 The deer was chased by the lion.

The lion chased the deer.

2 The book was written by a famous author.

_____

3 Some bread was made by the baker.

_____

Grammar

1 **Complete the sentences with words from the boxes.**

> has been   have been

> saving   sleeping   waiting
> studying   hurting

1 Dan _____ _____ to see the dentist for half an hour.

2 His tooth _____ _____ since yesterday.

3 It's time to wake up! You _____ _____ for hours.

4 The boys _____ _____ all their pocket money for ages.

5 Lucy _____ _____ for her exams since October.

2 **Make questions for the answers.**

1 How long _____

I have been learning English for six years.

2 _____

Yes, he has been working very hard.

3 Where _____

They have been living in Australia.

3 **Look and write.**

1

_They have been climbing for seven hours._____

2

_____ since nine o'clock.

3

I _____ all day.

4

It _____ all afternoon.

4 Look at the picture and read the notes.

Name: Manuel Blanco

Country of origin: Spain

Place of work: Sid's Super Circus

Number of years in circus: 10 years

First job: clown

Present job: horse trainer

Number of years in present job: 5 years

5 **A newspaper reporter, Lisa Hogan, is interviewing Manuel. Write her questions.**

Lisa: _____

Manuel: My name is Manuel Blanco.

Lisa: _____

Manuel: I come from Spain.

Lisa: _____

Manuel: I've been working in the circus for ten years.

Lisa: _____

Manuel: My first job was a clown.

Lisa: _____

Manuel: I train horses now.

Lisa: _____

Manuel: I've been training horses for five years.

Lisa: _____

Manuel: Yes, I love circus life.

Spelling

Remember. A **suffix** is a group of letters that we add to the **end** of a word.
use + ful = useful   use + less = useless

1 **Add *less* to each of these words.**
Now write the opposite of each word.

care	_careless_	_careful_
colour	_____	_____
pain	_____	_____
help	_____	_____
power	_____	_____
use	_____	_____

2 **Use the correct word to complete each sentence.**

1 When you drive a car you must be careful.

When you drive a car you must not be _____ .

2 A sharp pencil is useful.

A broken pencil is _____ .

3 I like to be helpful.

I don't like to be _____ .

4 A lion in the jungle is powerful.

A lion in a cage is _____ .

5 When I went to the dentist it was painless.

It was not _____ .

6 Anna's painting was very colourful

but Amy's picture was boring and _____ .

Writing

Make a poster to persuade people to join World Watch. Use this page to try out some of your ideas.

1 Colour the heading on the poster in bright colours.

2 Write some facts about World Watch. Keep each fact short.

World Watch stops pollution.

_____

_____

_____

_____

3 Choose the two facts you think are most important.
   Write each fact in a star on the poster. Colour in each star.

4 Think of a good picture to make people look at your poster.
   Here is a picture to give you some ideas.
   Draw your picture here. Do it in pencil first.

5 Think of a rhyme to end your poster.

THE WORLD IS IN DANGER !
JOIN WORLD WATCH TODAY!

Join World Watch! Make the world a better place.

Join World Watch! Put a smile _____

Check-up

1 Write the speech bubbles.

1 Sally said that she was thirsty.

2 Pete said that he was feeling ill.

3 Jack and Paul said that they could help.

4 Meg said that she had got a toothache.

2 Change the verbs.

1 'I'm watching TV.'   Bob said that he _____ TV.

2 'I can't speak Spanish.'   Sue said that she _____ Spanish.

3 'We enjoy football.'   The boys said that they _____ football.

4 'We are twins.'   The girls said that they _____ twins.

5 'I've got a kitten.'   Lucy said that she _____ a kitten.

3 Change the sentences.

1 The boys broke the window.

   The window was broken by the boys.

2 A cat ate the fish.

   _____

3 Many people saw the whales.

   _____

4 A team of divers found the wreck.

   _____

5 A clever thief stole the jewels.

   _____

4 **Complete the sentences with *for* or *since*.**

1 Ellie has worked in the library _____ 2003.

2 We have had our cat _____ six months.

3 Mr Scott has worked here _____ many years.

4 John and Jim have been friends _____ they were five years old.

5 **Look, read and write sentences.**

1

play – piano – two years
<u>She has played the piano for two years.</u>

2

work – pilots – last August

_____

3

be – ill – three days

_____

4

have – hat – years

_____

6 **Complete the sentences with words from the boxes.**

have been has been	watching shining working waiting

1 John _____ _____ very hard recently.

2 The sun _____ _____ all day.

3 We _____ _____ for a taxi for hours.

4 The girls _____ _____ TV since midday.

Comprehension

1 **Read pages 118–119 again. Write if each sentence is true or false.**

1 Kate was younger than James.   true

2 The machine made things larger or smaller.   _____

3 The banana grew 30 centimetres in length in the machine. _____

4 The print in the book became too small to read.   _____

5 James said that it was all right to play with the machine. _____

6 Two days later, Kate's friend came to play.   _____

7 Kate turned the handle of the machine when she
   showed it to Sara.   _____

8 Sara ran upstairs to the bathroom.   _____

9 James heard Sara talking to his Mum.   _____

10 James did not want to squash Kate.   _____

11 James sat on his bed and looked for Kate.   _____

12 Kate was happy to be small.   _____

Vocabulary

> Remember. A **noun** is a naming word. An **adjective** is a describing word. A **verb** is a doing word.

1 Find each of the words in the story on pages 118 and 119.
Fill in the missing vowels from each of these nouns.

1 c__nt__m__tr__

2 h__ndl__

3 __nv__nt__ __n

2 Fill in the missing vowels from each of these adjectives.

1 __mp__ss__bl__

2 l__ng

3 d__ng__r__ __s

3 Fill in the missing vowels from each of these verbs.

1 w__nd__r__d

2 b__c__m__

3 d__s__pp__ __r__d

4 Which of the words in exercises 1–3 above has:

one syllable? _____

two syllables? _____ _____ _____

three syllables? _____ _____ _____

four syllables? _____ _____

Language building

Remember. Sometimes we talk about the **gender** of a noun
boy has a **masculine** (male) gender.
girl has a **feminine** (female) gender.
doctor has a **common gender**. (A doctor can be male or female.)

1 **Write the feminine form of each masculine noun.**

1 boy _____girl_____   **2** man _____

3 brother _____   **4** husband _____

5 father _____   **6** uncle _____

7 nephew _____   **8** king _____

9 prince _____

2 **Answer these clues. (The answer is always a noun.) After each noun say if its gender is masculine (m), feminine (f) or common (c). Use the words in the box to help you.**

> daughter   driver   prince   inventor   father
> dentist   woman   king   librarian   princess

1 a person who looks after your teeth _____dentist_____ | c |

2 the son of a king _____ | |

3 the wife of a prince _____ | |

4 a person who works in a library _____ | |

5 a parent's female child _____ | |

6 the husband of your mother _____ | |

7 a person who drives a car _____ | |

8 the father of a princess _____ | |

9 a person who invents things _____ | |

10 the opposite of man _____ | |

Grammar

1 **What did James tell Kate to do?**

1 'Keep quiet!'   He told her to keep quiet.

2 'Watch carefully!'   _____

3 'Look at the machine!'   _____

4 'Be careful!'   _____

5 'Close the door.'   _____

2 **What did Kate tell James not to do?**

1 'Don't move!'   She told him to move.

2 'Don't be silly!'   _____

3 'Don't tell Mum!'   _____

4 'Don't talk so loudly!'   _____

5 'Don't touch anything!'   _____

3 **Complete the sentences using *told* or *asked*.**

1 'Sit down, please, everyone.'

She _____asked_____ them to sit down.

2 'Go away!'

He _____ me to go away.

3 'Please don't be angry!'

They _____ him not to be angry.

4 'Stand up!'

She _____ the class to stand up.

5 'Come here, please.'

I _____ you to come here.

4 Look at the pictures and answer the questions.

Give me the grapes!

You have a beautiful voice. Please, sing a song.

1   In picture 1 where was a crow sitting? What did he have in his beak?

2   In picture 2 which animal came along? Did he want the grapes?
    What did he tell the crow to do? Did the crow nod or shake his head?

3   In picture 3 what did the fox say? What did he ask the crow to do?

4   In picture 4 what did the crow do? What happened to the grapes?
    What did the fox do?

5 Write the story.

_____

_____

_____

_____

_____

_____

_____

_____

_____

_____

_____

Spelling

1 **Find the *wa* words.**

> Remember. Sometimes *a* sounds like *o* when it comes after *w*.
> wa**t**ch   swa**ll**ow

q	w	z	x	w	a	n	t	c	v	b	n
b	h	g	t	y	w	a	s	u	k	l	j
h	w	a	s	p	w	r	t	q	z	a	d
l	k	j	h	g	f	d	q	s	w	a	n
b	v	w	a	t	c	h	m	n	k	y	f
m	n	b	v	c	x	z	d	w	a	s	h
w	a	l	l	e	t	p	t	i	r	w	q
k	h	m	s	w	a	l	l	o	w	x	d

2 **Write the words in alphabetical order.**

1 _____   2 _____

3 _____   4 _____

5 _____   6 _____

7 _____   8 _____

3 **Choose the correct word from above to complete each sentence.**

1 I _____ my face with water.

2 I keep money in my _____ .

3 I _____ a new bike for my birthday.

4 A _____ is white and has got a long neck.

5 A _____ is yellow and black.

6 The girl _____ reading a book.

7 A _____ is like a small clock.

8 You put food in your mouth and _____ it.

Writing

1 **Label the picture of the cat. Use the words in the box.**

| sharp claws | paws | teeth like needles | tail |
| pointed ears | long whiskers | green eyes | fur |

2 **Circle the words which mean 'very big'.** Use the dictionary to help you.

tiny   huge   enormous   small   gigantic

3 **Here are some verbs about the way a cat moves. Find out what they mean.**

creep   crawl   leap   jump

Imagine that Kate met a gigantic cat! Write your own story. Write about:
- What the cat looked like to Kate. • How Kate felt.
- What she thought. • What the cat did. • What Kate did.

Remember to write in paragraphs!

(Continue in your copy book if you do not have enough space on this page.)

Kate and the gigantic cat

James tried to make Kate bigger again – but the machine did not work! He left Kate in the room and went downstairs. Just then a huge cat appeared ...

_____

_____

_____

_____

_____

_____

_____

_____

_____

_____

_____

_____

_____

_____

_____

_____

_____

_____

_____

_____

_____

_____

_____

_____

Unit

Comprehension

1 Read pages 126–127 again.
There is something wrong
with each sentence.
Write each sentence
correctly.

1 John Logie Baird invented the telephone.

_____

2 John Logie Baird was born in England.

_____

3 He was very clever at school.

_____

4 John wanted his four friends to have their own television system.

_____

5 John built a glider (a plane with an engine), and took it onto his roof.

_____

6 He learned to be an engineer.

_____

7 Once he tried to make gold with electricity.

_____

8 Between 1927 and 1929 he sent moving pictures from one place to
another.

_____

_____

9 He sent moving pictures across the Indian Ocean to America.

_____

Vocabulary

Remember. Words that **sound alike** but have **different meanings** are called **homophones**.

1 **Match up the pairs of words that sound the same.**

1 ate	c	**a** write	**6** to		**f** sale
2 meat		**b** see	**7** pair		**g** sun
3 right		**c** eight	**8** sail		**h** pear
4 sea		**d** steel	**9** son		**i** their
5 steal		**e** meet	**10** there		**j** two

2 **Write the pairs of words here.**

1 ___ate, eight___

2 _____

3 _____

4 _____

5 _____

6 _____

7 _____

8 _____

9 _____

10 _____

3 **Choose the correct word for each sentence.**

1 I sat down _____ (to, two) watch TV.

2 I _____ (ate, eight) a sandwich.

3 Do you eat _____ (meat, meet)?

4 A _____ (pair, pear) is a fruit.

5 I can _____ (right, write) neatly.

6 The ship has got a _____ (sail, sale).

7 Sharks live in the _____ (sea, see).

8 Mr Baird's _____ (son, sun) was called John.

9 It is wrong to _____ (steal, steel).

10 The boys rode _____ (there, their) bikes.

Language building

A **compound sentence** can be made up of **two simple sentences**. A simple sentence can also be called a **main clause**.
(main clause 1)   (conjunction)   (main clause 2)
John Logie Baird experimented   and   he invented television.
Sometimes we can leave out the **subject** of the second clause.
John Logie Baird experimented and (he) invented television.

1 **Fill in the missing subject from the second clause of each compound sentence.**

1 Mr Baird was an inventor and _____ (he, she) invented many things.

2 Anna was good at maths but _____ (he, she) was no good at sport.

3 The dog chased the boy and _____ (he, it) barked loudly.

4 The car went too fast and _____ (it, she) crashed into a wall.

5 The lady loved cakes but _____ (he, she) didn't like chocolate.

6 The children played football and _____ (we, they) rode their bikes.

7 You can draw but _____ (you, we) can't paint very well.

8 We climbed the tree and _____ (you, we) picked some apples.

9 I can't whistle but _____ (I, we) can sing.

2 **Now write each compound sentence above as two separate main clauses.**

1 John Logie Baird was an inventor. He invented many things.

2 _____

3 _____

4 _____

5 _____

6 _____

7 _____

8 _____

9 _____

Grammar

1 **Complete the sentences with *have to*. Be careful! Use the correct form of the verb.**

1 John _____ get up at six o'clock every morning.

2 Tomorrow he _____ get up at five.

3 The weather was so bad yesterday that we _____ stay at home.

4 I spilled juice on my homework. Look! I _____ to do it all again.

5 You always _____ be careful when you cross the road.

2 **Make questions for the answers.**

1 _____

No, we don't have to go to school on Saturdays.

2 Why _____

He had to buy a new mobile because his old one was broken.

3 How long _____

They will have to travel for eight hours.

4 When _____

He has to leave for school at 7.30.

5 _____

Yes, she has had to work really hard recently.

3 **What are they saying? Use *have to*. Be careful to use the correct form!**

1

'_____ every day.'

2

'_____ a uniform to school.'

3

'_____ last week.'

4 **Professor Muddle is going on holiday to Italy. He is very forgetful so he has made a list of important things to remember. His list is in a terrible muddle. Can you help him?**

Don't forget!!

airport – check in luggage

toothbrush – suitcase   Rome – take photos

passport – pocket   camera – suitcase

send postcards   show passport and tickets

tickets - pocket   speak Italian!!

5 **Think about these questions.**

1 Before he left home, he had to do four things. What were they?

2 He is at the airport now. What does he have to do? Find two things.

3 When he gets to Italy, what will he have to do? Find three things.

6 **Write.**

Before Professor Muddle left home, he _____

_____

_____

_____

He is at the airport now. He _____

_____

_____

When he gets to Italy, he _____

_____

_____

_____

Spelling

Remember. The **i** in some words sounds like **ee**.

an onion

1 In each word an *i* is missing. Spell each word correctly.

1 opinon _____opinion_____ **2** rado _____

3 brillant _____ **4** materal _____

5 onon _____ **6** audence _____

7 mysterous _____ **8** millon _____

9 obedent _____ **10** alen _____

2 Write all the words from above in the chart.

words where *i* comes before *a*	words where *i* comes before *e*	words where *i* comes before *o*

3 Choose the correct word for each sentence.

1 I heard some music on the _____ (alien / radio).

2 I like _____ (onion / opinion) in my dinner.

3 The _____ (material / audience) liked the film.

4 The population of Greece is more than ten _____ (mysterious / million).

5 When the teacher said, 'Stop talking,' the children were quiet.

They were very _____ (obedient / brilliant).

Writing

I think zoos are good because you see lots of animals from different parts of the world. Some animals are nearly extinct. Zoos keep these animals alive. You can learn a lot about animals at a zoo.

I disagree. I think zoos are bad. It is not kind to keep wild animals in cages. Zoos cannot give animals a natural life. Animals are unhappy in zoos.

1 **Make your own list of the advantages and disadvantages of zoos. Try to think of at least five points for each.**

Advantages

Zoos contain animals from all over the world.

Disadvantages

It is not kind to keep animals in cages.

2 **Write an argument _for_ zoos or _against_ them. Use the page opposite to help you.**

Do you think zoos are good or bad? Remember!
- State your point of view clearly at the beginning.
- Begin a new paragraph. Give several reasons to support your point of view.
- Begin another paragraph. Be fair. Give one reason which supports the opposite point of view.
- Write a final paragraph. State one or two more reasons which support your opinion.

Zoos are _____ .

I think zoos are _____ . I have several reasons to support

my point of view.

My first reason is that _____

_____

_____

_____

My second reason is _____

_____

_____

_____

Another reason why I think zoos are _____ is that

_____

_____

_____

Some people do not agree. They think zoos are _____ .

They think _____ .

However, on the whole I think zoos are _____ because

_____

_____

_____

_____

_____

Unit  Comprehension

1 **Read pages 134–135 again. Answer these questions.**

1 Who went into the jungle first?

_____

2 What was the path covered over with?

_____

3 Where did they stop for the night?

_____

4 What was at the edge of the clearing?

_____

5 What did they make their beds with?

_____

6 Why must the fire burn all night?

_____

7 What animal did the boy hear crying far away?

_____

8 Why did the boy hold his teeth tightly together?

_____

9 What did the boy hold above his head?

_____

10 What made the boy feel better?

_____

Vocabulary

Remember. An **antonym** is a word with the opposite meaning. Use the thesaurus on page 166 of Language Book 5 to help you with this activity.

1 **Rewrite each sentence. Make it mean the opposite. Replace the underlined words with antonyms.**

1 John <u>preceded</u> Anna.

_____

2 I felt <u>ashamed</u> of being poor.

_____

3 I <u>finished</u> reading the book.

_____

4 The armchair was very <u>comfortable</u>.

_____

5 I was <u>afraid</u> of the darkness.

_____

6 We crossed the <u>wide</u> river.

_____

7 The guide spoke in a <u>calm</u> voice.

_____

8 It was <u>gloomy</u> in the jungle.

_____

Language building

> Remember! We can write speech in **two ways**.
> a **direct speech**: Old Mali said, 'Fire frightens animals.'
>   Old Mali's exact words are used. Speech marks are used.
> b **reported speech**: Old Mali said that animals are frightened of fire.
>   Old Mali's exact words are not used. No speech marks are used.

1 **Write if each sentence contains direct speech (D) or reported speech. (R)**

1 'Collect some wood,' Old Mali said. ☐

2 Sam told Old Mali that he was afraid of the dark. ☐

3 'I don't like the jungle,' Sam cried. ☐

4 'I'll look after you,' Old Mali said to Sam. ☐

5 Sam said that he saw a tiger in the bush. ☐

6 Old Mali told Sam that there were no tigers in the jungle. ☐

2 **Change the first sentence from direct speech to reported speech. Finish the second sentence in each pair.**

1 'My knife is very sharp,' Sam said.

 Sam said that _____.

2 Old Mali said, 'Yesterday I heard a snake in the grass.'

 Old Mali said that _____.

3 'Not all snakes are dangerous,' Old Mali told Sam.

 Old Mali told Sam that _____.

4 Sam said, 'I read a book to help me stay awake.'

 Sam said that _____.

5 'Sit near the fire with me,' Old Mali said to Sam.

 Old Mali told Sam to _____.

6 Sam said, 'I made my bed from soft moss.'

 Sam said that he _____.

Grammar

1 **Complete the sentences. Use the words in the box.**

is she?   are you?   isn't it?   are we?   aren't they?   isn't he?

1 It's cold today, _____

2 John's playing well, _____

3 You're not enjoying this film, _____

4 The children are very quiet, _____

5 Anna isn't here today, _____

6 We're not going shopping, _____

2 **Finish these sentences in the same way.**

1 We're going to Greece, _____

2 Those boys aren't French, _____

3 It isn't a good idea, _____

4 Jane is an excellent singer, _____

5 You're good at basketball, _____

6 That man isn't a pilot, _____

3 **Look at the pictures and write sentences in the same way.**

1

_____ , _____

2

_____ , _____

3

_____ , _____

4

_____ , _____

4 Amy is looking at her holiday photos with her friend, Sue. Look at the photos. Answer each question and add one more sentence.

1

2

3

4

1 Photo 1: Sue: What's this place?

Amy: _____

Sue: _____ , isn't it?

2 Photo 2: Sue: What are these?

Amy: _____

Sue: _____ , aren't they?

3 Photo 3: Sue: What are you doing?

Amy: _____

Sue: _____ , aren't you?

4 Photo 4: Sue: What's your dad doing?

Amy: _____

Sue: _____ , isn't he?

Spelling

Remember. The prefix **pre** often means 'in front of' or 'before'. The prefix **mis** often means 'badly' or 'wrong'.
pre + fix = prefix
mis + spell = misspell

1 Add the correct prefix (*pre* or *mis*) to the beginning of each word.

1 <u>mis</u> behave   <u>misbehave</u>   2 ____fix   _____

3 ____pare   _____   4 ____spell   _____

5 ____view   _____   6 ____understand   _____

7 ____use   _____   8 ____cede   _____

2 Use the words above to complete the crossword.

clues down↓

1 to go in front of

3 to spell wrong

4 to look at something before anyone else can see it

5 to behave badly

clues across →

1 letters that go in front of a word

2 to get things ready

5 not to understand something

6 to use something badly

Writing

If the information is not in the story or you can't see it in any of the pictures in the story, guess it!

1 **Make some notes about Jeff (the boy in the story on pages 134–135). Fill in the chart below.**

Boy's name: _____

Physical appearance (how he looks):

- age _____
- height _____
- face _____
- clothes _____

  _____

- anything else? _____

  _____

Personality (the sort of person he is e.g. quiet, helpful) _____

_____

Skills (what he's good at doing; say anything he's <u>not</u> good at, too!)

_____

_____

Relationships (how he gets on with Old Mali; the way he talks to him etc.)

_____

_____

Things he likes and dislikes

_____

_____

2 **Write a description of Jeff. Use your notes to help you.**

A description of Jeff

Jeff is a boy. He is about _____ years old. He is about _____ tall.

Jeff has got a _____ face and _____ hair.

Jeff is wearing _____

_____

_____

Jeff always likes to help. He is a _____ boy. _____

_____

_____

Jeff is good at _____

_____

_____

Jeff is not good at _____

_____

_____

Jeff gets on well with Old Mali. He _____

_____

_____

Jeff likes adventure. He enjoys _____

_____

_____

Jeff does not like _____

_____

_____

Unit  17

Comprehension

1 **Read pages 142–143 again. Choose the correct answer for each gap.**

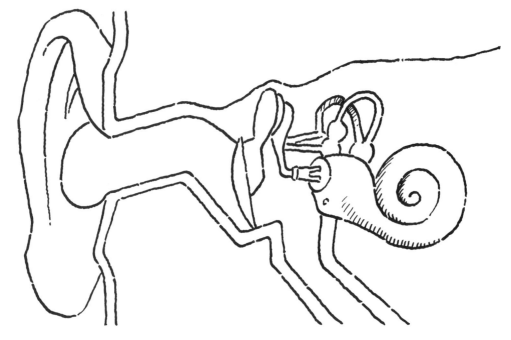

1 We _____ (see, smell, hear) sounds.

2 A sound makes the air _____ (wave, vibrate, spin).

3 Sound waves travel down your _____ (earhole, throat, back).

4 Your ear drum moves very _____ (slowly, quickly, noisily) when sound waves hit it.

5 Your ear drum is joined to three _____ (teeth, nerves, bones).

6 The bones in your ear are very _____ (hard, large, tiny).

7 Inside your ear you have three _____ (cubes, tubes, tubs).

8 The tubes in your ear contain watery _____ (food, drink, liquid).

9 Your _____ (brain, head, eye) tells you what a sound is.

10 The watery liquid inside the tubes in your ear help you to _____ (dance, sleep, balance).

Vocabulary

Remember. We can add to the **beginning** or **ending** of some words to make them longer. We call these words **root words**. e.g. hear: hearing, mishear

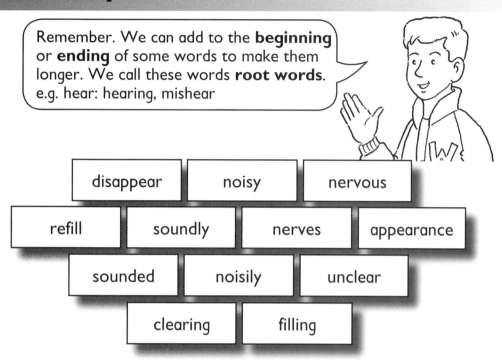

disappear	noisy	nervous
refill	soundly	nerves	appearance
sounded	noisily	unclear
clearing	filling

1 **Write the pairs of words in the wordwall that come from each root word.**

nerve _____ _____

sound _____ _____

noise _____ _____

clear _____ _____

fill _____ _____

appear _____ _____

2 **Which words have a suffix added at the end?**

___*noisy*___ _____ _____ _____

_____ _____ _____ _____

3 **Which words have a prefix added at the beginning?**

__*disappear*__ _____ _____

Language building

> We can change some **verbs** into **nouns** by adding a **suffix**.
> The strings of a guitar vibrate. (vibrate = verb)
> The vibration of the air is called a sound wave. (vibration = noun)

1 **Change each verb into a noun ending with *tion* or *ment*. Be careful with the spelling!**

1 vibrate   ___vibration___   2 evaporate   _____

3 advertise   _____   4 agree   _____

5 educate   _____   6 enjoy   _____

7 improve   _____   8 decorate   _____

2 **Write the *tion* nouns in alphabetical order.**

_____   _____   _____   _____

3 **Write the *ment* nouns in alphabetical order.**

_____   _____   _____   _____

4 **Choose the correct *ment* noun from above to complete each sentence.**

1 I ate the ice cream with great _____ .

2 I saw an _____ for a new TV in the magazine.

3 We made an _____ not to argue with each other again.

4 My teacher said there was an _____ in my writing.

5 **Choose the verb or noun to complete each sentence.**

1 The skirt had a spotty _____ (decorate, decoration) on

2 Drum skins _____ (vibrate, vibration) when you hit them with a stick.

3 The heat of the sun makes water _____ (evaporate, evaporation).

4 My school gives me a good _____ (educate, education).

Grammar

1 **Complete the sentences with the words in the boxes.**

> used to

> hear   play   live   like   have   be

1 When Alfie was small, his family _____ _____ by the sea.
2 Miss Timms _____ _____ a nurse but now she is a teacher.
3 I _____ _____ a camera but I lost it.
4 We _____ _____ wolves at night but not any more.
5 Bill and Ben _____ _____ football but now they prefer tennis.
6 You _____ _____ swimming. What do you like now?

2 **Write the sentences again. Change the underlined verb and use 'used to'.**

1 He <u>rode</u> a bike but now he drives a car.

_____

2 I <u>spoke</u> Italian but not any more.

_____

3 We often <u>went</u> abroad for our holidays.

_____

4 Miss Grey <u>taught</u> Maths but now she teaches Science.

_____

5 You <u>hated</u> eating vegetables but now you like them.

_____

6 The boys <u>swam</u> every day but now they swim once a week.

_____

3 **Look at the pictures and read.**

This is Martin Green. When he was young, he had very little money but he worked very hard and now he is rich.

4 **Write about Martin. Try to include these verbs:**

be   wear   have   ride   drive   keep

From rags to riches

Martin Green used to be poor but now he is rich.

_____

_____

_____

_____

_____

_____

_____

_____

_____

_____

Spelling

When **or** comes after **w** it often sounds like **er**, e.g. w**or**k
When **ar** comes after **w** it often sounds like **or**, e.g. w**ar**drobe

1 Choose *ar* or *or* to complete each word.

1 w __ __ m

2 w __ __ m

3 w __ __ d

4 sw __ __ m

5 w __ __ drobe

6 w __ __ k

7 w __ __ ld

8 w __ __ se

9 w __ __ n

10 rew __ __ d

2 Choose the correct word from above to complete each sentence.

1 I put my clothes in the _____ in my bedroom.

2 I always _____ very hard at school.

3 A _____ is made of letters.

4 A _____ lives under the ground.

5 There are many countries in the _____ .

6 It is _____ in the sun.

7 There was a _____ of bees in the garden.

8 My writing is not good. I am _____ at writing than reading.

9 The lady gave me a _____ when I found her ring.

10 I tried to _____ my friend that there was a shark coming towards him!

Writing

1 Label the picture diagram of the guitar.

neck   strings   body   head

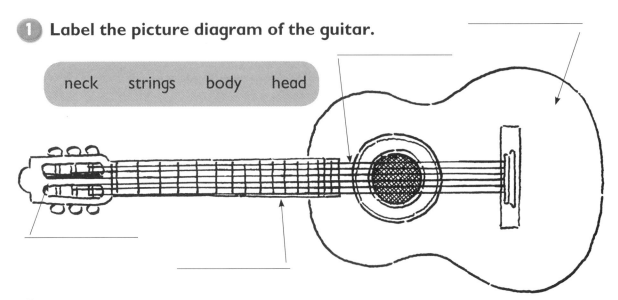

2 Complete this flow diagram. It explains how a guitar works.

ear   vibrates   guitar   move   hears

strings   brain   soundwaves

A _____ has got six _____ .

↓

When you pluck a string, it _____ .

↓

These vibrations make the air _____ . _____
move through air to your _____ .

↓

Your ear _____ the sound waves.

↓

Your _____ tells you the sound waves
are sounds from a guitar.

3

Write an explanation. Explain how a drum works.

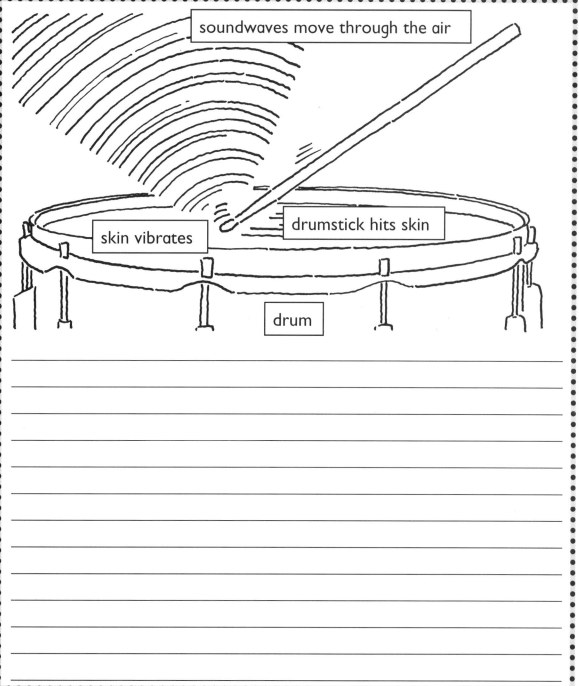

soundwaves move through the air

drumstick hits skin

skin vibrates

drum

_____
_____
_____
_____
_____
_____
_____
_____
_____
_____
_____
_____
_____
_____

Unit  18

Comprehension

1 **Read pages 150 and 151 again.**

2 **Answer the questions about *The Five Senses Shop*.**

1 What smells in the forest? _____

2 What feels soft? _____

3 What melts in your mouth? _____

4 What looks beautiful? _____

5 What makes a sighing sound? _____

3 **Answer the questions about *The Sound of the Night*.**

1 Fill in the missing verbs:

_____ in bed,

_____ out the light,

_____ your eyes

Really tight.

_____ to the

Sounds of the night.

2 What was the first sound the poet heard? _____

3 What was the poet's sister doing? _____

4 What was the poet's brother doing? _____

5 Who was at the door? _____

6 What animal did the poet hear? _____

7 What was in the sky? _____

8 What was the weather like? _____

Vocabulary

Remember. Some words tell us about the sounds things make.

1 **Choose the correct verb to complete each sentence.**

1 Ducks _____ (cluck, quack).

2 Cows _____ (coo, moo).

3 Bees _____ (sing, buzz).

4 Owls _____ (howl, hoot).

5 Mice _____ (squeak, speak).

6 Frogs _____ (creak, croak).

7 Dogs _____ (bark, bellow).

8 Cats _____ (meow, mumble).

9 Horses _____ (neigh, bray).

10 Sheep _____ (bleat, beat).

11 Hens _____ (quack, cluck).

We can add the suffix **ing** to each verb above to change it into a noun:
the quacking of a duck

2 **Fill in the correct nouns below.**

In the countryside I can hear:

the _buzzing_ of bees,   the _____ of cats,

the _____ of cows,   the _____ of dogs,

the _____ of ducks, the _____ of frogs,

the _____ of horses,   the _____ of hens,

the _____ of mice, the _____ of owls,

the _____ of sheep.

Language building

Remember. A **sentence tag** is something we add to the **beginning** or **end** of a sentence. Always use a **comma** before or after a sentence tag.

BB

I like the taste of apples, do you?   Yes, I do.

1 **Underline the sentence tag in each sentence. Put in the missing comma in each sentence.**

1 The music is too loud, <u>I think</u>.

2 I like the smell of bread do you?

3 I can hear a clock ticking can you?

4 The taste of ice cream is nice isn't it?

5 Look out a car is coming.

6 Sarah do you want a drink?

7 Sorry Miss.

8 Please stop shouting Amy.

9 Can I go now please?

10 That's my pen the red one.

2 **Put in the missing commas in this little play. Underline the sentence tag in each sentence.**

Mum: Do you want to go to the shopping mall Anna?

Anna: Yes I do.

Mum: We'll go this afternoon I think.

Anna: Oh good that gives me time to finish my book.

Mum: You like reading don't you?

Anna: It's my favourite subject at school Mum.

Mum: I'm pleased about that very pleased.

Anna: Can we go to the bookshop in town please?

Mum: For a treat I'll buy you a new book to read.

Anna: Wow that's great!

Grammar

1 **Match the sentences and write the letters.**

1 You've worked very hard, children.
2 She can't walk.
3 We had a wonderful party.
4 Look at John's boat.
5 You've passed your exam!
6 I bought a big bunch of flowers.
7 Look at the monkey!
8 The children spun round and round.

a We really enjoyed ourselves.
b You should be proud of yourself.
c It's looking at itself in the water.
d Give yourselves a clap!
e They made themselves dizzy.
f He made it all by himself.
g I think she's hurt herself.
h It was a present for myself.

1 _____ 2 _____ 3 _____ 4 _____ 5 _____ 6 _____ 7 _____ 8 _____

2 **Choose the right word to complete the sentences.**

1 There's plenty to eat, Joe. Please help _____ .
(himself / yourself)

2 Are you listening? Or am I talking to _____ ?
(myself / yourself)

3 Be careful, boys. Take care of _____ .
(themselves / yourselves)

4 We don't need any help. We can do it by _____ .
(ourselves / itself)

3 **Look at the pictures and write. Use the verbs in brackets.**

1 (feed)   <u>The baby is feeding himself.</u>

2 (look)   _____

3 (wash)   _____

4 (sing)   _____

4 **Look at the pictures and think about these questions.**

1 What sort of nest was there in the reeds? How many eggs were in it?

2 How many ducklings hatched out? What was strange about one of them?

3 Did the little ducklings laugh at the big one? What did they say?

4 Did the ugly duckling stay with the others or go away? Where did he hide himself?

5 What did he do in spring? Were the other ducks surprised? What did they tell him to do?

6 What did the ugly duckling do? What did he see?

5 **Write the story.**

_____

_____

_____

_____

_____

_____

_____

_____

_____

_____

Spelling

Remember. **Homophones** are words that sound the same but have got different meanings.

a stair   a stare

1 **Write a word that sounds the same as each word below, but has a different meaning.**

1 plane ___plain___

2 steal _____

3 right _____

4 weight _____

5 knows _____

6 peace _____

7 rode _____

8 pear _____

2 **Choose the correct words to complete the sentences.**

1 The shirt did not have a pattern on it. It was very _____ (plane / plain).

2 It is wrong to _____ (steal / steel).

3 You _____ (right / write) with a pen.

4 I can't _____ (wait / weight) for my birthday to come.

5 My friend _____ (knows / nose) where I live.

6 Can I have a _____ (peace / piece) of cake?

7 I have got a _____ (pear / pair) of white socks.

8 I _____ (road / rode) my bike on the _____ (road / rode).

Writing

Sit very still for five minutes. Listen carefully to all the sounds you can hear. Make a note of the sounds below.

The sounds I can hear

After five minutes, stop. Check the spelling of any words you wrote that you are not sure about. Tick the ten sounds that you think were most interesting.

1 Write a list poem about the sounds heard.

1 Think of a good title.

2 Think of a good way to begin your poem.

3 Write your list poem. Use the ten sounds you ticked. Write them in any order you like. Use your best handwriting. Your poem does not have to rhyme.

4 Think of a good way to end your poem.

5 You can draw some pictures on a separate sheet.

Check-up

1 **What did the teacher tell her class?**

1 'Come in, children!' <u>She told</u> **2** 'Sit down quickly!' _____

<u>them to come in.</u> _____

3 'Don't make a noise!' _____ **4** 'Get out your books!' _____

_____ _____

5 'Write carefully!' _____ **6** 'Don't make any mistakes!' _____

_____ _____

2 **Complete the sentences with _told_ or _asked_.**

1 'Please, be quiet!'

She _____ the children to be quiet.

2 'Fetch the ball, Rover!'

The boy _____ the dog to fetch the ball.

3 'Don't speak so fast, please!'

The teacher _____ me not to speak so fast.

4 'Don't move, Jane!'

I _____ Jane not to move.

3 **Complete the sentences with _have to_. Be careful! Use the correct form of the verb.**

1 You _____ brush your teeth every night before you go to bed.

2 Yesterday the children _____ get to school early.

3 It is going to rain tomorrow. I _____ take an umbrella.

4 Susie is learning the piano. She _____ practise every day.

5 Recently we _____ work very hard.

6 At his last school Joe _____ not _____ wear a uniform.

4 **Complete the sentences.**

1 You're not feeling very well, <u>are you?</u> _____

2 Anna is a good singer, _____

3 The boys aren't playing in the rain, _____

4 We're going to visit Grandma tomorrow, _____

5 John isn't interested in sport, _____

5 **Write the sentences again. Change the underlined verb and use** *used to.*

1 He <u>was</u> a good footballer but now he can't play.

_____

2 Jane <u>had</u> long hair but now it is very short.

_____

3 I <u>liked</u> football but now I prefer basketball.

_____

4 We <u>went</u> to Spain but now we spend our holidays in Greece.

_____

6 **Choose the right word to complete the sentences.**

1 The girl is looking at _____ in the mirror.
   (itself / herself)

2 Are you enjoying _____ , children?
   (yourself / yourselves)

3 John can't walk. He has hurt _____ .
   (himself / myself)

4 What a silly mistake! I'm so angry with _____ !
   (myself / itself)

5 Nobody helped them. They did it by _____ .
   (ourselves / themselves)

Final Check-up

1 **Complete the sentences with the correct form of the verbs.**

1 Billy usually _____ to school by bus. (go)

2 Yesterday he _____ on foot. (go)

3 We _____ never _____ a dolphin. (see)

4 Sally _____ her exams next year. (take)

5 At the moment the children _____ TV. (watch)

2 **Make questions for the answers.**

1 _____

Yes, she likes to play tennis.

2 What _____

Those boys speak Spanish.

3 Where _____

They went to Greece.

4 When _____

He'll arrive at midday.

5 _____

No, they aren't studying.

3 **Rewrite the sentences in the negative.**

1 The children were playing. _____

2 My uncle bought a new car. _____

3 Tigers live in Africa. _____

4 You ought to wear sandals. _____

5 They will enjoy the film. _____

6 That dog barks a lot. _____